Medieval and Early Modern Times

Active Reading Note-Taking Guide

Teacher Edition

Douglas Fisher, Ph.D.
San Diego State University

New York, New York Columbus, Ohio Chicago, Illinois Peoria, Illinois Woodland Hills, California

About the Author

Douglas Fisher, Ph.D., is a Professor in the Department of Teacher Education at San Diego State University. He is the recipient of an International Reading Association Celebrate Literacy Award as well as a Christa McAuliffe award for excellence in teacher education. He has published numerous articles on reading and literacy, differentiated instruction, and curriculum design as well as books, such as *Improving Adolescent Literacy: Strategies at Work* and *Responsive Curriculum Design in Secondary Schools: Meeting the Diverse Needs of Students.* He has taught a variety of courses in SDSU's teacher-credentialing program as well as graduate-level courses on English language development and literacy. He has also taught classes in English, writing, and literacy development to secondary school students.

The McGraw·Hill Companies

Send all inquiries to:
Glencoe/McGraw-Hill
8787 Orion Place
Columbus, OH 43240-4027

ISBN 0-07-870265-8

Printed in the United States of America.

3 4 5 6 7 8 9 10 024 09 08 07 06

Table of Contents

Letter to the Student v
Letter to the Teacher vii

Chapter 1 Roman Civilization
- **Section 1-1:** Life in Ancient Rome 1
- **Section 1-2:** The Fall of Rome 6
- **Section 1-3:** The Byzantine Empire 11

Chapter 2 Islamic Civilization
- **Section 2-1:** The Rise of Islam 17
- **Section 2-2:** Islamic Empires 22
- **Section 2-3:** Muslim Ways of Life 28

Chapter 3 Medieval Africa
- **Section 3-1:** The Rise of African Civilizations 33
- **Section 3-2:** Africa's Religion and Government 38
- **Section 3-3:** African Society and Culture 44

Chapter 4 China in the Middle Ages
- **Section 4-1:** China Reunites 49
- **Section 4-2:** Chinese Society 54
- **Section 4-3:** The Mongols in China 59
- **Section 4-4:** The Ming Dynasty 64

Chapter 5 Medieval Japan
- **Section 5-1:** Early Japan 69
- **Section 5-2:** Shoguns and Samurai 75
- **Section 5-3:** Life in Medieval Japan 82

Chapter 6 Medieval Europe
- **Section 6-1:** The Early Middle Ages 87
- **Section 6-2:** Feudalism 92
- **Section 6-3:** Kingdoms and Crusades 97
- **Section 6-4:** The Church and Society 103
- **Section 6-5:** The Late Middle Ages 109

Chapter 7 The Renaissance
- **Section 7-1:** The Renaissance Begins 113
- **Section 7-2:** New Ideas and Literature 119
- **Section 7-3:** Renaissance Art 124

Chapter 8 The Reformation
- **Section 8-1:** The Reformation Begins 129
- **Section 8-2:** The Reformation Spreads 135
- **Section 8-3:** The Counter-Reformation 140

Chapter 9 The Americas
- **Section 9-1:** The First Americans 145
- **Section 9-2:** Life in the Americas 150
- **Section 9-3:** The Fall of the Aztec and Inca Empires 157

Table of Contents

Chapter 10 The Age of Exploration

Section 10-1: Europe Explores the World 161
Section 10-2: Trade and Empire 167
Section 10-3: A Global Exchange 172

Chapter 11 The Age of Enlightenment

Section 11-1: The Scientific Revolution 177
Section 11-2: The Ideas of the Enlightenment 184
Section 11-3: Politics and the Enlightenment 189

Answer Key 195

To the Student

Dear Social Studies Student,

Can you believe it? The start of another school year is upon you. How exciting to be learning about different cultures, historical events, and unique places in your social studies class! I believe that this* Active Reading Note-Taking Guide *will help you as you learn about your community, nation, and world.

Note-Taking and Student Success

Did you know that the ability to take notes helps you become a better student? Research suggests that good notes help you become more successful on tests because the act of taking notes helps you remember and understand content. This *Active Reading Note-Taking Guide* is a tool that you can use to achieve this goal. I'd like to share some of the features of this *Active Reading Note-Taking Guide* with you before you begin your studies.

The Cornell Note-Taking System

First, you will notice that the pages in the *Active Reading Note-Taking Guide* are arranged in two columns, which will help you organize your thinking. This two-column design is based on the **Cornell Note-Taking System**, developed at Cornell University. The column on the left side of the page highlights the main ideas and vocabulary of the lesson. This column will help you find information and locate the references in your textbook quickly. You can also use this column to sketch drawings that further help you visually remember the lesson's information. In the column on the right side of the page, you will write detailed notes about the main ideas and vocabulary. The notes you take in this column will help you focus on the important information in the lesson. As you become more comfortable using the **Cornell Note-Taking System**, you will see that it is an important tool that helps you organize information.

The Importance of Graphic Organizers

Second, there are many graphic organizers in this *Active Reading Note-Taking Guide*. Graphic organizers allow you to see the lesson's important information in a visual format. In addition, graphic organizers help you understand and summarize information, as well as remember the content.

Research-Based Vocabulary Development

Third, you will notice that vocabulary is introduced and practiced throughout the *Active Reading Note-Taking Guide*. When you know the meaning of the words used to discuss information, you are able to understand that information better. Also, you are more likely to be successful in school when you have vocabulary knowledge. When researchers study successful students, they find that as students acquire vocabulary knowledge, their ability to learn improves. The *Active Reading Note-Taking*

To the Student

Guide focuses on learning words that are very specific to understanding the content of your textbook. It also highlights general academic words that you need to know so that you can understand any textbook. Learning new vocabulary words will help you succeed in school.

Writing Prompts and Note-Taking

Finally, there are a number of writing exercises included in this *Active Reading Note-Taking Guide*. Did you know that writing helps you to think more clearly? It's true. Writing is a useful tool that helps you know if you understand the information in your textbook. It helps you assess what you have learned.

You will see that many of the writing exercises require you to practice the skills of good readers. Good readers *make connections* between their lives and the text and *predict* what will happen next in the reading. They *question* the information and the author of the text, *clarify* information and ideas, and *visualize* what the text is saying. Good readers also *summarize* the information that is presented and *make inferences* or *draw conclusions* about the facts and ideas.

I wish you well as you begin another school year. This *Active Reading Note-Taking Guide* is designed to help you understand the information in your social studies class. The guide will be a valuable tool that will also provide you with skills you can use throughout your life.

I hope you have a successful school year.

Sincerely,

Douglas Fisher

To the Teacher

Dear Social Studies Teacher,

As you begin a new school year, one of the biggest challenges you will probably encounter is getting students to read their textbooks. Informational text can overwhelm students, leaving them less likely to read and more likely to become apathetic about learning. I believe that this* Active Reading Note-Taking Guide *will help students use their textbooks more effectively as they learn about their community, nation, and world.

Note-Taking and Student Success

There is considerable research evidence that addresses how students understand difficult concepts and content in school. Glencoe/McGraw-Hill has developed the *Active Reading Note-Taking Guide* for social studies students based upon that research. Evidence indicates that students need to know how to take notes, use graphic organizers, learn vocabulary, and develop their thinking skills by writing in order to achieve academic success.

Did you know that the ability to take and organize notes predicts how well students will do in school? Peverly, Brobst, Graham, and Shaw (2003) showed that when students use background knowledge and take notes, they are likely to perform well on tests. Pauk (1974) observed that note-taking was a critical skill for college success. Notes serve as an external storage function (meaning on the paper) that builds comprehension and content understanding (Ganske, 1981). This *Active Reading Note-Taking Guide* is a tool that students can use to achieve this goal. I would like to share some of the features of this *Active Reading Note-Taking Guide* with you before you begin teaching.

The Cornell Note-Taking System

First, you will notice that the pages in the *Active Reading Note-Taking Guide* are arranged in two columns, which will help students organize their thinking. This two-column design is based on the **Cornell Note-Taking System,** developed at Cornell University. Faber, Morris, and Lieberman (2000) found that the Cornell Note-Taking System improves comprehension and increases test scores.

The column on the left side of the page highlights the main ideas and vocabulary of the lesson. This column will help students find information and locate the references in their textbooks quickly. Students can also use this column to sketch drawings that help them visually remember the lesson's information. In the column on the right side of the page, students will write detailed notes about the main ideas and vocabulary. The notes they take in this column will help them focus on the important information in the lesson. As students become more comfortable using the Cornell Note-Taking System, they will see that it is an important tool that helps them organize information.

The Importance of Graphic Organizers

Second, there are many graphic organizers in this *Active Reading Note-Taking Guide*. Graphic organizers allow students to see the lesson's important information in a visual format. In addition, graphic organizers help students summarize information and remember the content. I hope that you will encourage students to use the graphic organizers because they will help them understand what they are reading.

To the Teacher

Research-Based Vocabulary Development

Third, you will notice that vocabulary is introduced and practiced throughout the *Active Reading Note-Taking Guide*. When students know the meaning of the words used to discuss information, they are able to understand that information better. Also, students are more likely to be successful in school when they have vocabulary knowledge. When researchers study successful students, they find that as students acquire vocabulary knowledge, their ability to learn improves (Martino and Hoffman, 2002). The *Active Reading Note-Taking Guide* focuses on learning words that are very specific to understanding the content of the textbook. The guide also highlights general academic words that students need to know so that they can understand *any* textbook. These vocabulary words are based on the Academic Word List (AWL) developed by Averil Coxhead. The AWL includes the most common 570 words found in academic texts, excluding the 2,000 general English words such as *the, in,* and *that*. Research indicates that students who master the words on Coxhead's list score significantly higher on standardized tests.

Writing Prompts and Note-Taking

Finally, there are a number of writing exercises included in this *Active Reading Note-Taking Guide*. Writing is a useful tool that helps students understand the information that is being presented. Writing helps them to assess what they have learned. You will see that many of the writing exercises require students to practice the skills of good readers. Good readers *make connections* between their lives and the text and *predict* what will happen next in the reading. They *question* the information and the author of the text, *clarify* information and ideas, and *visualize* what the text is saying. Good readers also *summarize* the information that is presented and *make inferences* or *draw conclusions* about the facts and ideas.

I wish you well as you begin another school year. This *Active Reading Note-Taking Guide* is designed to help students understand the information in your social studies class. The guide will be a valuable tool that will also provide students with skills that they can use throughout their lives.

I hope you have a successful school year.

Sincerely,

Douglas Fisher

References

Faber, J. E., Morris, J. D., and Lieberman, M. G. (2000). The effect of note taking on ninth grade students' comprehension. *Reading Psychology,* 21, 257–270.

Ganske, L. (1981). Note-taking: A significant and integral part of learning environments. *Educational Communication and Technology: A Journal of Theory, Research, and Development,* 29, 155–175.

Martino, N. L., and Hoffman, P. R. (2002). An investigation of reading and language abilities of college freshmen. *Journal of Research in Reading,* 25, 310–318.

Pauk, W. (1974). *How to Study in College*. Boston: Houghton Mifflin.

Peverly, S. T., Brobst, K. E., Graham, M., Shaw, R. (2003). College adults are not good at self-regulation: A study on the relationship of self-regulation, note taking, and test taking. *Journal of Educational Psychology,* 95, 335–346.

Van Leeuwe, J., and Aarnoutse, C. (1998). Relation between reading comprehension, vocabulary, reading pleasure, and reading frequency. *Educational Research and Evaluation,* 4, 143–166.

Chapter 1, Section 1
Life in Ancient Rome

(Pages 136–143)

Main Idea

Setting a Purpose for Reading Think about these questions as you read:

- How did Augustus create a new era of prosperity?
- What ideas did the Romans borrow from the Greeks?

Reading Strategy

As you read pages 137–143 in your textbook, complete this Venn diagram to show similarities and differences between Roman culture and Greek culture.

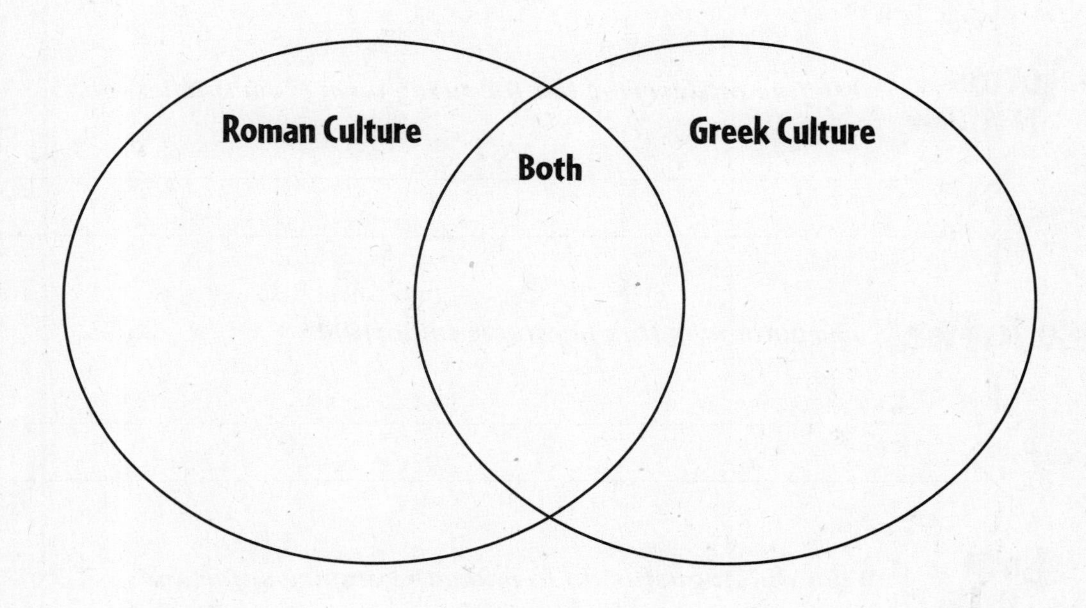

A Prosperous Empire *(pages 137–138)*

Drawing Conclusions

Augustus paved the way for 200 years of peace and prosperity. Why do you think the Roman Empire remained at peace even with weak emperors such as Caligula and Nero?

Terms To Know

Define or describe the following term from this lesson.

Pax Romana

People To Meet

Explain why this person is important.

Augustus

Sum It Up

What did Augustus do to make the empire safer and stronger?

Roman Culture *(pages 139–143)*

Synthesizing

Roman historians took different views of the Roman Empire. After you read the entire passage, read the views of Livy and Tacitus again (page 140). Now you play the historian. Using all you have read and learned about Rome up to this point, write your own view of the empire.

Terms To Know

Define or describe the following terms from this lesson.

vault

satire

ode

anatomy

aqueduct

Stoicism

Key Points | Notes

People To Meet

Explain why these people are important.

Virgil

Horace

Galen

Ptolemy

Academic Vocabulary

Define these academic vocabulary words from this lesson.

distinct

emphasis

Sum It Up

How did the Romans improve on Greek ideas in architecture?

Now that you have read the section, write the answers to the questions that were included in* Setting a Purpose for Reading *at the beginning of the lesson.

How did Augustus create a new era of prosperity?

____

____

____

____

____

____

What ideas did the Romans borrow from the Greeks?

____

____

____

____

____

____

Read To Write Challenge

Roman culture, government, and religion were heavily influenced by the Greeks. On a separate sheet of paper, write an* expository essay *describing the Roman influence on modern civilization.

Chapter 1, Section 2
The Fall of Rome

(Pages 144–153)

Main Idea

Setting a Purpose for Reading Think about these questions as you read:
- Why was the Roman Empire weakened?
- How would our world be different today if the Roman Empire had never existed?

Reading Strategy

As you read pages 145–153 in your textbook, complete the diagram showing the causes of the fall of the Roman Empire.

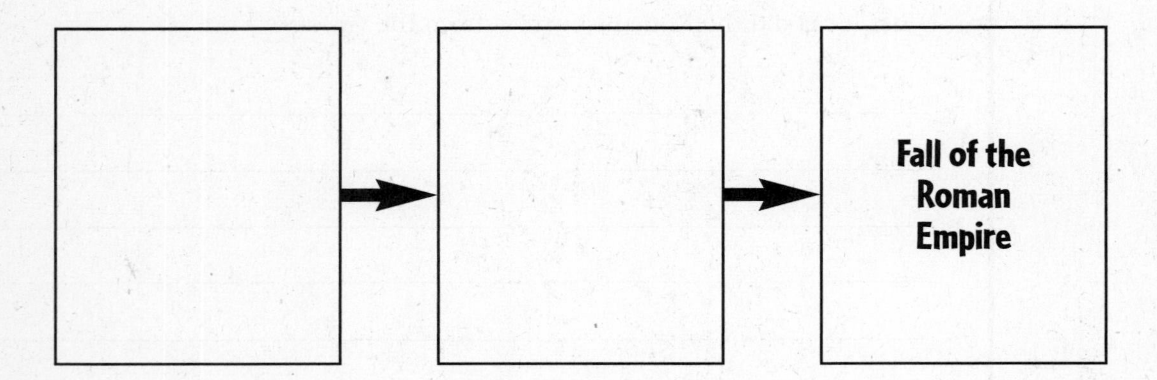

The Decline of Rome *(pages 145–147)*

Summarizing

Use the chart below to summarize the reforms made by Diocletian and Constantine.

Diocletian's Reforms	Constantine's Reforms

Terms To Know

Define or describe the following terms from this lesson.

inflation

barter

reform

Places To Locate

Briefly describe the following place.

Constantinople

Academic Vocabulary

Define these academic vocabulary words from this lesson.

stable

purchase

Sum It Up ***How did Diocletian try to reverse the decline of Rome?***

Rome Falls *(pages 149–151)*

Scanning ***Glance quickly over the reading to find answers to the following questions.***

1. What happened to the empire in A.D. 395?

2. Why did Germanic groups invade the empire?

3. What happened at the Battle of Adrianople?

4. Who was Alaric?

5. Who was Odoacer?

Key Points | Notes

People To Meet

Explain why this person is important.

Theodosius

Sum It Up

Which event usually marks the fall of the Western Roman Empire?

The Legacy of Rome *(pages 152–153)*

Reviewing

Use the chart below to take notes on the legacies of Rome. Use your completed chart to review key concepts from your reading.

The Legacy of Rome		
Government	**Culture**	**Religion**

Academic Vocabulary

Define this academic vocabulary word from this lesson.

consider

Key Points

Notes

Sum It Up

Which aspects of the Roman Empire are reflected in present-day cultures?

Section Wrap-up

Now that you have read the section, write the answers to the questions that were included in **Setting a Purpose for Reading** ***at the beginning of the lesson.***

Why was the Roman Empire weakened?

How would our world be different today if the Roman Empire had never existed?

Read To Write Challenge

Research to learn about inflation. On a separate sheet of paper, write an **expository essay** ***describing the causes and effects of inflation on the decline of the Roman empire.***

Chapter 1, Section 3
The Byzantine Empire

(Pages 156–165)

Main Idea

Setting a Purpose for Reading Think about these questions as you read:

- What policies and reforms made the Byzantine Empire strong?
- What ideas and beliefs shaped Byzantine culture?

Reading Strategy

As you read pages 157–165 in your textbook, complete this chart to show the causes and effects of Justinian's new law code.

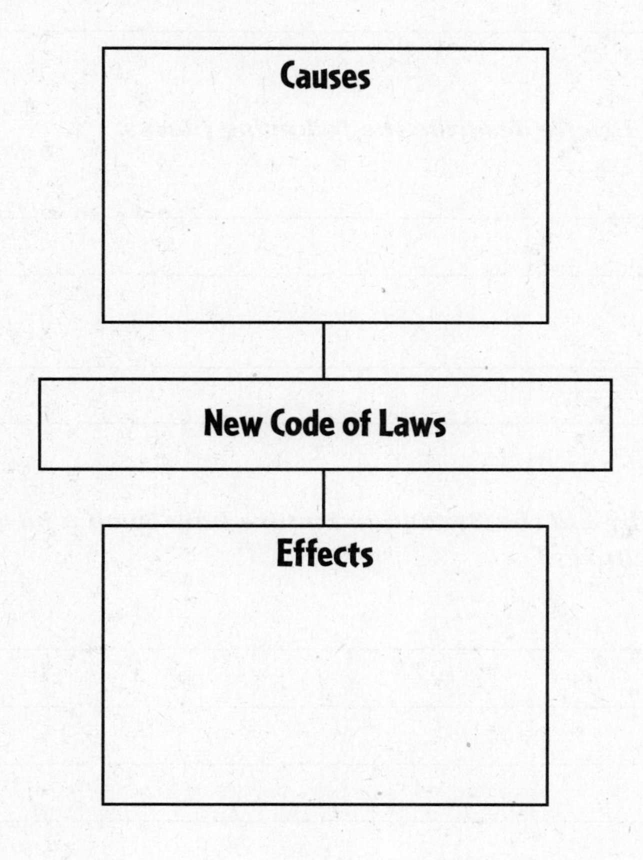

The Rise of the Byzantines *(pages 157–158)*

Previewing

Preview this section to get an idea of what is ahead. First, skim the section. Then write a sentence or two explaining what you think you will be learning. After you have finished reading, revise your statements as necessary.

Places To Locate

Briefly describe the following places.

Black Sea

Aegean Sea

Sum It Up

Why did the Byzantine Empire have such a blending of cultures?

Emperor Justinian *(pages 158–159)*

Determining the Main Idea

As you read, write the main idea of the passage. Review your statement when you have finished reading and revise as needed.

People To Meet

Explain why these people are important.

Justinian

Theodora

Belisarius

Tribonian

Academic Vocabulary

Define this academic vocabulary word from this lesson.

utilize

Sum It Up

What did Justinian accomplish during his reign?

The Byzantine Church *(pages 161–162)*

Summarizing

As you read, look for the reasons for the conflicts that led to the break between the Roman Catholic and Eastern Orthodox churches. Then, after you read, use the chart below to summarize the major reasons for the split.

Church Conflicts

____

____

____

____

Academic Vocabulary

Define this academic vocabulary word from this lesson.

image

____

____

Sum It Up

How did church and government work together in the Byzantine Empire?

____

____

____

Byzantine Civilization *(pages 163–165)*

Outlining

Complete this outline as you read.

I. The Importance of Trade

A. ______________________________

B. ______________________________

II. Byzantine Art and Architecture

A. ______________________________

B. ______________________________

III. Byzantine Women

A. ______________________________

B. ______________________________

IV. Byzantine Education

A. ______________________________

B. ______________________________

Terms To Know

Define or describe the following terms from this lesson.

mosaic

____

saint

____

regent

____

Academic Vocabulary

Define this academic vocabulary word from this lesson.

stress

____

Sum It Up

What church is one of Justinian's greatest achievements?

____

Now that you have read the section, write the answers to the questions that were included in* Setting a Purpose for Reading *at the beginning of the lesson.

What policies and reforms made the Byzantine Empire strong?

What ideas and beliefs shaped Byzantine culture?

Read To Write Challenge

Research to learn more about icons. On a separate sheet of paper, write a* comparative essay *describing the arguments for and against the use of icons in the Church of the Byzantine Empire.

Chapter 2, Section 1
The Rise of Islam

(Pages 174–180)

Main Idea

Setting a Purpose for Reading Think about these questions as you read:
- How did geography shape the Arab way of life?
- What did Muhammad teach?

Reading Strategy

As you read pages 175–180 in your textbook, complete this diagram to identify the Five Pillars of the Islamic faith.

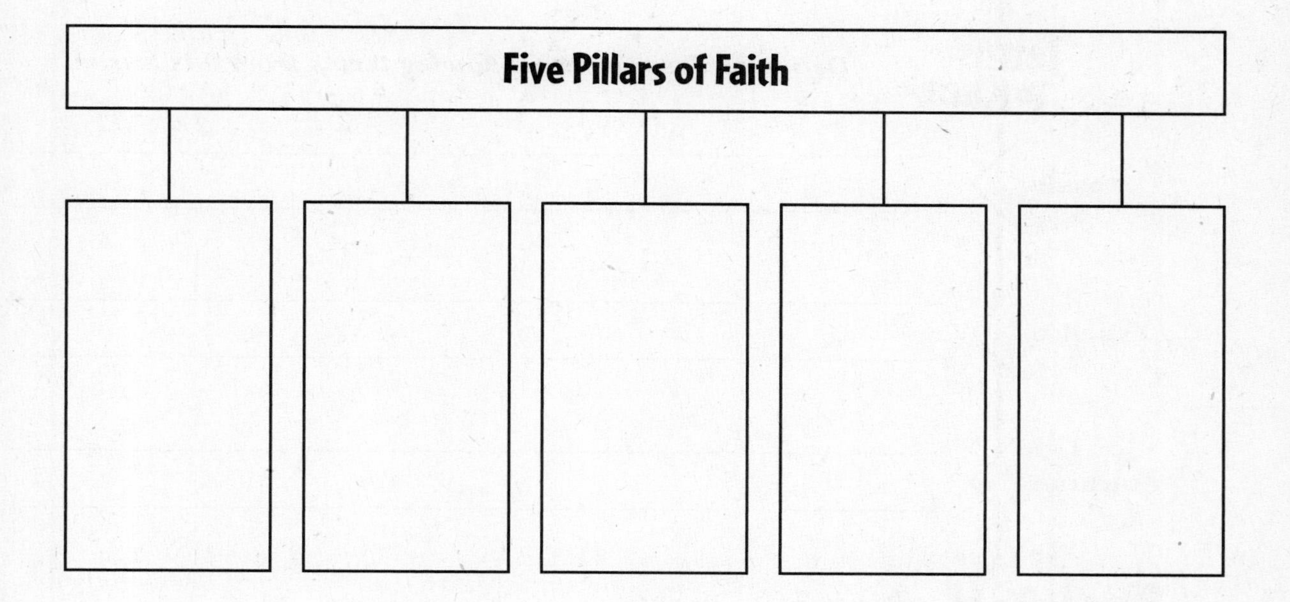

Daily Life in Early Arabia *(pages 175–176)*

Responding

Picture yourself in the deserts of Arabia. The heat is intense. Water is scarce. You live life as a Bedouin, traveling from oasis to oasis. What do you experience in a day? What do you like about your life? What do you not like? After you read the passage, write a paragraph about your life.

Terms To Know

Define or describe the following terms from this lesson.

oasis

sheikh

caravan

People To Meet

Explain why this group is important.

Bedouins

Places To Locate

Briefly describe the following places.

Makkah

Kaaba

Academic Vocabulary

Define these academic vocabulary words from this lesson.

intense

transport

Sum It Up

How did geography shape life in Arabia?

Muhammad: Islam's Prophet *(pages 176–177)*

Questioning

As you read, write three questions about the main ideas presented in the text. After you finish reading, write the answers to these questions.

1.

2. ______________________________

3. ______________________________

Places To Locate *Briefly describe the following place.*

Madinah ______________________________

Sum It Up *Why did Muhammad's message appeal to the poor?*

____

Islam's Teachings *(pages 179–180)*

Previewing *Before you read, look over the passage. What do you already know about Islam? What do you want to learn about Islam? Complete the first two columns in the table below. Then, after you read, fill in the third column with new information you learned.*

What I know about Islam	What I want to learn about Islam	What I learned about Islam

Terms To Know

Define or describe the following term from this lesson.

Quuran

Sum It Up

What role do the Quran and Sunna play in Muslim daily life?

Section Wrap-up

Now that you have read the section, write the answers to the questions that were included in **Setting a Purpose for Reading** ***at the beginning of the lesson.***

How did geography shape the Arab way of life?

What did Muhammad teach?

Read To Write Challenge

One of the five pillars of Islam requires each Muslim to pray five times a day facing Makkah. On a separate sheet of paper, write an **expository essay** ***explaining the importance of Makkah to Muslims.***

Chapter 2, Section 2
Islamic Empires

(Pages 181–189)

Main Idea

Setting a Purpose for Reading Think about these questions as you read:

- How did Islam spread?
- Why did Muslims split into two groups?

Reading Strategy

As you read pages 182–189 in your textbook, complete the diagram to show why the Arabs were successful conquerors.

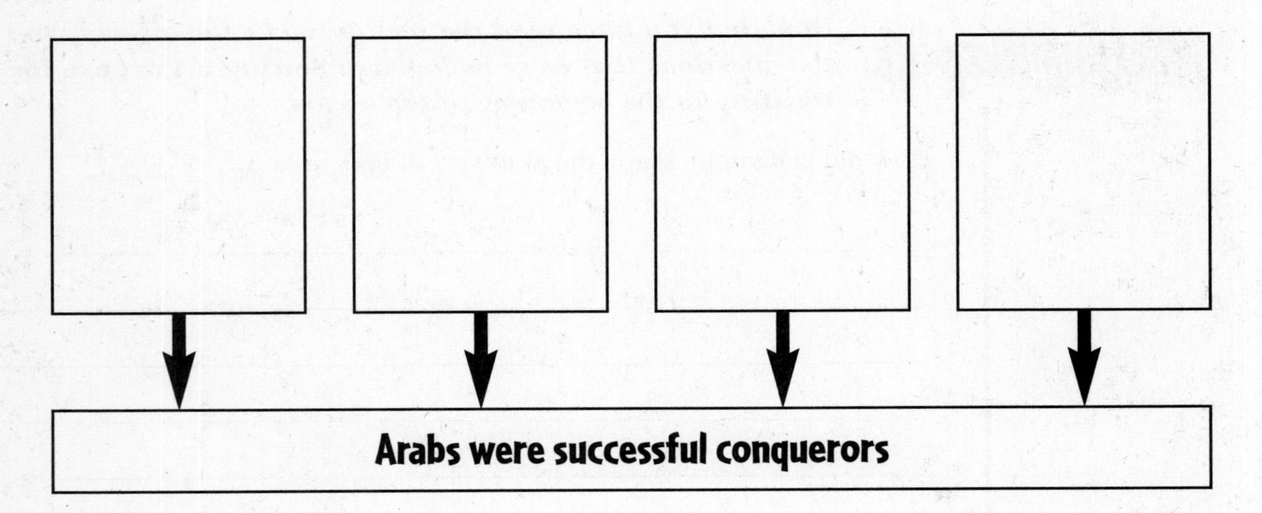

The Spread of Islam *(pages 182–184)*

Determining the Main Idea

As you read, write the main idea of the passage. Review your statement when you finish reading, and revise as needed.

Terms To Know

Define or describe the following term from this lesson.

caliph

People To Meet

Explain why these people are important.

Umayyad

Sufi

Places To Locate

Briefly describe the following places.

Damascus

Indonesia

Timbuktu

Sum It Up

How did Arabs spread the religion of Islam through trade?

____

____

____

____

Struggles Within Islam *(pages 185–186)*

Sequencing

As you read, number the following rulers and dynasties in the correct order.

1. ____ Umayyads

2. ____ Muhammad

3. ____ Seljuks

4. ____ Mongols

5. ____ Abbasids

Terms To Know

Define or describe the following terms from this lesson.

Shiite ____

____

Sunni ____

____

sultan ____

____

People To Meet

Explain why this group is important.

Abbasids

Places To Locate

Briefly describe the following place.

Baghdad

Academic Vocabulary

Define these academic vocabulary words from this lesson.

policy

devote

Sum It Up

What is the difference between Shiite and Sunni Muslims?

Later Muslim Empires *(pages 187–189)*

Reviewing

As you read, fill in the information in the chart below. Use this chart to review information about the Ottoman and Mogul empires.

	Ottoman Empire	Mogul Empire
Great leader		
Location		
Capital		
Accomplishments		

People To Meet

Explain why these people are important.

Suleiman I

Moguls

Akbar

Places To Locate

Briefly describe the following place.

Delhi

Academic Vocabulary

Define these academic vocabulary words from this lesson.

style

____

____

impose

____

____

Sum It Up

How did Constantinople change in 1453?

____

____

____

Section Wrap-up

Now that you have read the section, write the answers to the questions that were included in **Setting a Purpose for Reading** ***at the beginning of the lesson.***

How did Islam spread?

____

____

____

Why did Muslims split into two groups?

____

____

____

Read To Write Challenge

Reread the quote by Ibn Khaldun on page 186 in your textbook. On a separate sheet of paper, write a **narrative essay** ***in the voice of Khaldun explaining what he means by the phrase "A person who lacks the power to do a thing is never told to do it."***

Chapter 2, Section 3
Muslim Ways of Life

(Pages 190–197)

Main Idea

Setting a Purpose for Reading Think about these questions as you read:

- What was Muslim society like?
- How did Muslims contribute to science and culture?

Reading Strategy

As you read pages 191–197 in your textbook, complete this pyramid to show the social classes in the early Muslim world.

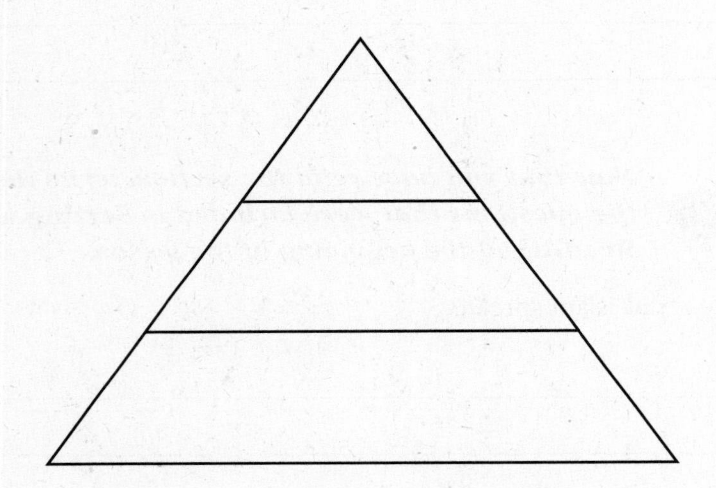

Trade and Everyday Life *(pages 191–193)*

Inferring

Why would language and coins make trade easier for the Muslims? Write your answer in the space below.

Terms To Know

Define or describe the following terms from this lesson.

mosque

bazaar

Academic Vocabulary

Define this academic vocabulary word from this lesson.

widespread

Sum It Up

How did the Muslim rulers give their merchants an advantage?

Muslim Achievements *(pages 193–197)*

Scanning

Before you read, scan the passage looking for information to include in the table below. After you read, add information to complete the table.

Muslim Achievements		
Math and Science	**Writing**	**Art and Buildings**

Terms To Know

Define or describe the following terms from this lesson.

minaret

crier

Academic Vocabulary

Define this academic vocabulary word from this lesson.

innovate

People To Meet

Explain why these people are important.

Mamun

al-Razi

Ibn Sina

Omar Khayyam

Ibn Khaldun

Places To Locate

Briefly describe the following places.

Granada

Agra

Sum It Up

What contributions did Muslims make in math and science?

Now that you have read the section, write the answers to the questions that were included in **Setting a Purpose for Reading** *at the beginning of the lesson.*

What was Muslim society like?

How did Muslims contribute to science and culture?

Read To Write Challenge

Research to learn about how Islam influenced Muslim art. On a separate sheet of paper, write a **comparative essay** *describing the difference between Byzantine and Muslim art.*

Chapter 3, Section 1
The Rise of African Civilizations

(Pages 206–214)

Main Idea

Setting a Purpose for Reading Think about these questions as you read:
- How did geography affect the development of African kingdoms?
- What factors contributed to the growth of African civilizations?

Reading Strategy

As you read pages 207–214 in your textbook, complete this diagram showing the accomplishments of medieval African civilizations.

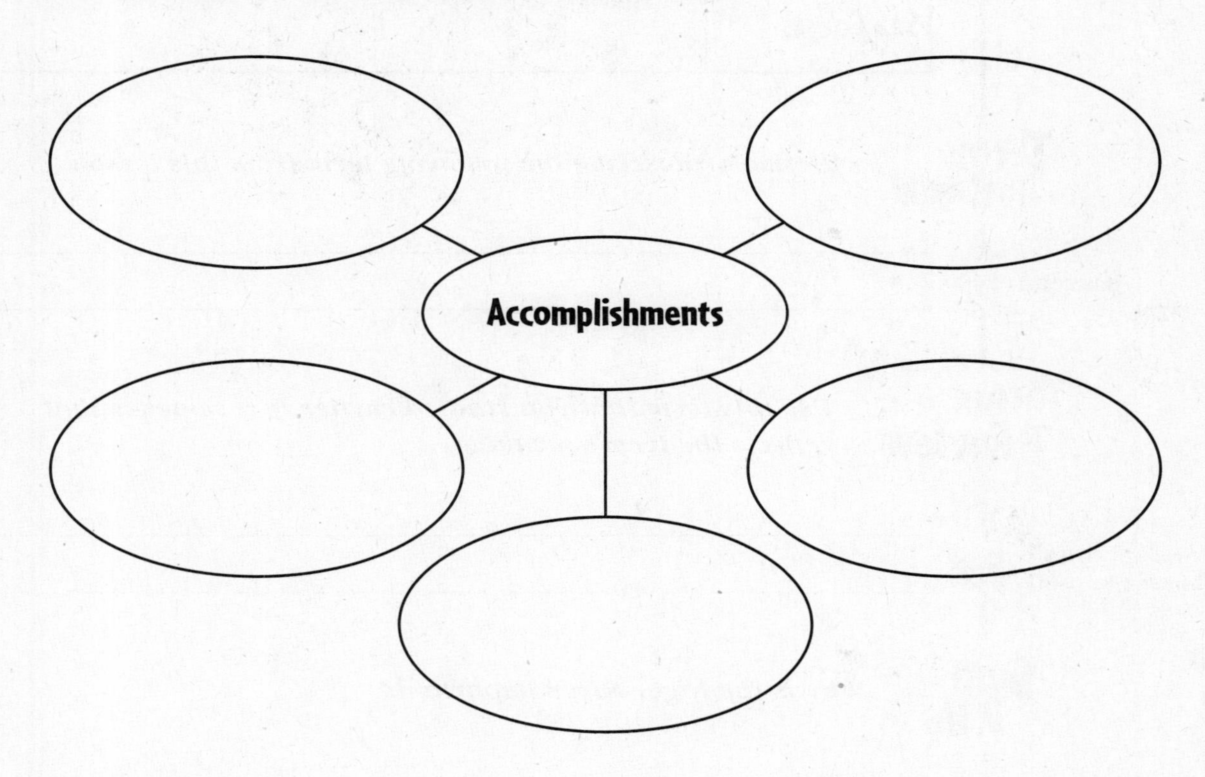

Africa's Geography *(pages 207–208)*

Summarizing

As you read, picture yourself in the different parts of the African continent. Complete the chart below with a summary of each part of Africa. As you write, think about what it would be like to explore each of these very different places.

Tropics	
Deserts	
Rain Forests	
Mediterranean Sea Coasts	

Terms To Know

Define or describe the following term from this lesson.

plateau

___

___

Terms To Review

Use this term that you studied earlier in a sentence that reflects the term's meaning.

oasis
(Chapter 2, Section 1)

___

___

Sum It Up

Why is the Niger River important?

___

___

___

___

African Trading Empires *(pages 209–214)*

Questioning

As you read, write three questions about the main ideas presented in the text. After you finish reading, write the answers to these questions.

1. ____

2. ____

3. ____

Terms To Know

Define or describe the following terms from this lesson.

griot ____

dhow ____

Academic Vocabulary

Define these academic vocabulary words from this lesson.

fee ____

diminish

prime

People To Meet

Explain why these people are important.

Sundiata Keita

Mansa Musa

Sunni Ali

Places To Locate

Briefly describe the following places.

Benue River

Ghana

Mali

Timbuktu

Songhai

Axum

Sum It Up

Why did West Africa become the center of three large trade empires?

Section Wrap-up

Now that you have read the section, write the answers to the questions that were included in **Setting a Purpose for Reading** ***at the beginning of the lesson.***

How did geography affect the development of African kingdoms?

What factors contributed to the growth of African civilizations?

Read To Write Challenge

The Bantu are considered the ancestors of much of Africa. On a separate sheet of paper, write a **persuasive essay** ***listing evidence of this common heritage.***

Chapter 3, Section 2
Africa's Religion and Government

(Pages 222–229)

Main Idea

Setting a Purpose for Reading Think about these questions as you read:

- What religions and beliefs shaped life in Africa?
- How did African governments develop?

Reading Strategy

As you read pages 223–229 in your textbook, complete the diagram to show the characteristics of Swahili culture and language.

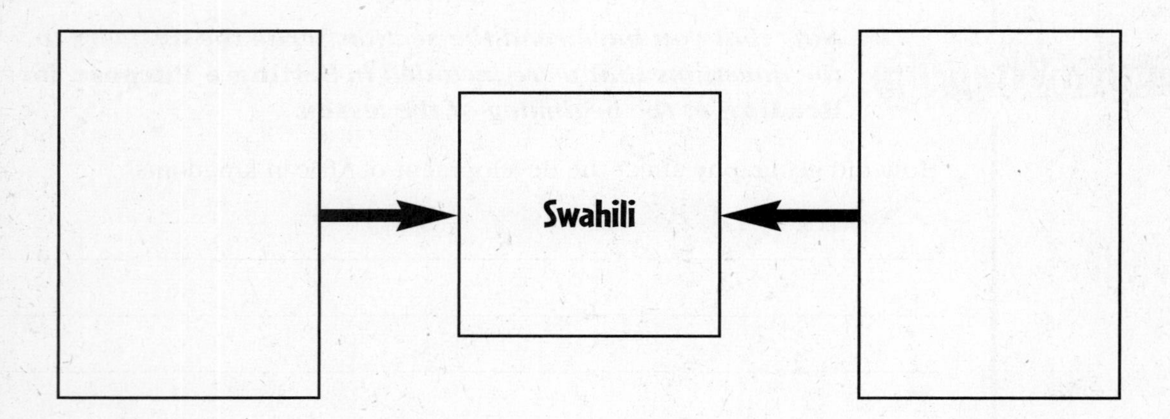

Traditional African Religions *(page 223)*

Drawing Conclusions

As you read, take notes in the space below on the different African religious practices and beliefs. Then answer the question below:

Why do you think Africans held so strongly to their own religious practices?

People To Meet

Explain why this person is important.

Olaudah Equiano

Academic Vocabulary

Define this academic vocabulary word from this lesson.

vary

Sum It Up

What was the role of ancestors in African religion?

Key Points

Islam in Africa *(pages 224–227)*

Analyzing

As you read, fill in the information in the chart below. Use this chart to review information about Mansa Musa's and Askia Muhammad's role in strengthening the Islamic religion.

Growth of Islam	
Mansa Musa	**Askia Muhammad**

Terms To Know

Define or describe the following terms from this lesson.

sultan

Swahili

People To Meet

Explain why these people are important.

Ibn Battuta

Askia Muhammad

Places To Locate

Briefly describe the following place.

Makkah

Academic Vocabulary

Define these academic vocabulary words from this lesson.

accompany

element

Terms To Review

Use each of these terms that you studied earlier in a sentence that reflects the term's meaning.

Quran
(Chapter 2, Section 1)

mosque
(Chapter 2, Section 3)

Sum It Up

How did Askia Muhammad gain control of Songhai?

Government and Society *(pages 227–229)*

Visualizing

Imagine you are a citizen of Ghana. You have a complaint against your neighbor. You just brought your complaint before the king. Write a paragraph about your meeting with the king. What did you do? What did he do? How did you feel as you approached the king? What was happening around you?

Terms To Know

Define or describe the following term from this lesson.

clan

Academic Vocabulary

Define this academic vocabulary word from this lesson.

benefit

Sum It Up

How was Mali ruled differently from Ghana?

Now that you have read the section, write the answers to the questions that were included in* Setting a Purpose for Reading *at the beginning of the lesson.

What religions and beliefs shaped life in Africa?

____

____

____

____

____

____

How did African governments develop?

____

____

____

____

____

____

Read To Write Challenge

Islam spread to much of Africa along trade routes. On a separate sheet of paper, write a* narrative essay *from the perspective of a traditional African ruler deciding whether to convert to Islam.

Chapter 3, Section 3
African Society and Culture

(Pages 230–237)

Main Idea

Setting a Purpose for Reading Think about these questions as you read:

- What events shaped the culture of medieval Africa?
- What effects has African culture had on other cultures around the world?

Reading Strategy

As you read pages 231–237 in your textbook, complete this Venn diagram to show the similarities and differences between the enslavement of Africans in Africa and the enslavement of Africans in Europe.

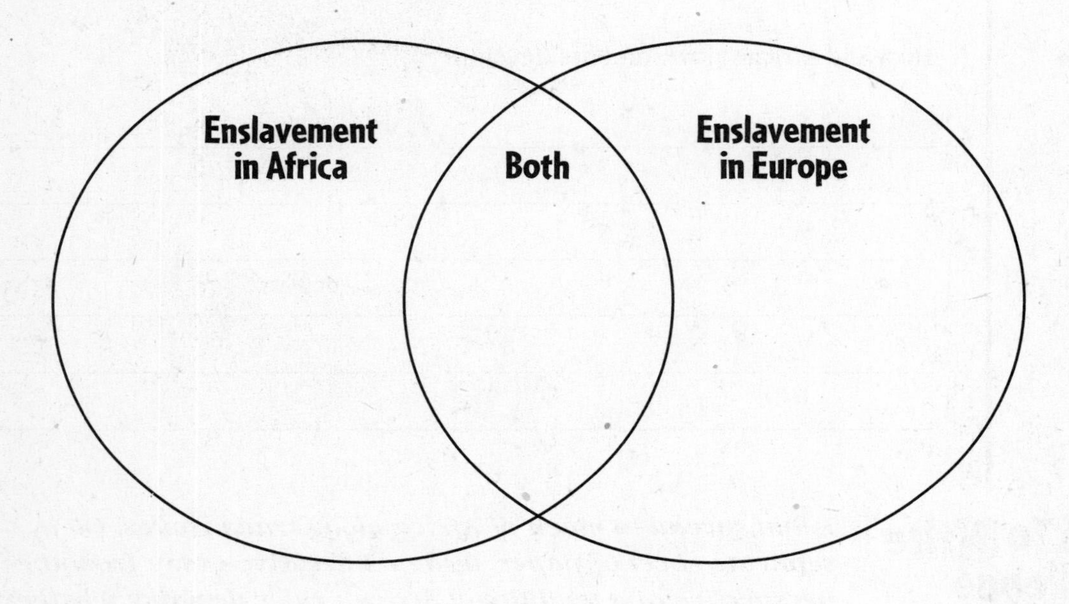

Life in Medieval Africa *(pages 231)*

Connecting

In West Africa, griots told stories passed down from generation to generation as part of the community's oral history. What stories have been passed down from generation to generation in your family or community? How has this story affected you? Write the story—your oral history—and your response to it in the space below.

Terms To Know

Define or describe the following terms from this lesson.

extended family

matrilineal

oral history

People To Meet

Explain why these people are important.

Dahia al-Kahina

Nzinga

Academic Vocabulary

Define this academic vocabulary word from this lesson.

bond

Terms To Review

Use this term that you studied earlier in a sentence that reflects the term's meaning.

griot
(Chapter 3, Section 1)

Sum It Up

How were Bantu families organized?

Slavery *(pages 233–234)*

Previewing

Preview this section to get an idea of what is ahead. First, skim the section. Then write a sentence or two explaining what you think you will learn. After you finish reading, revise your statements as necessary.

Academic Vocabulary

Define this academic vocabulary word from this lesson.

release

Sum It Up

How did exploration change the African slave trade?

African Culture *(pages 235–237)*

Synthesizing

How has African culture affected your world today? As you read, note the different types of African dance, art, stories, and music in the passage. Then think about how you see African dance, art, and music in the world around you today. Write a brief paragraph about the effects of African culture in your society today.

Sum It Up

Why did Africans use dance to celebrate important events?

Section Wrap-up

Now that you have read the section, write the answers to the questions that were included in **Setting a Purpose for Reading** *at the beginning of the lesson.*

What events shaped the culture of medieval Africa?

What effects has African culture had on other cultures around the world?

Read To Write Challenge

Africans had enslaved their fellow Africans for centuries before the Portuguese captured their first Africans to sell as slaves. On a separate sheet of paper, write an* expository essay *about how the slave trade changed in Africa.

Chapter 4, Section 1
China Reunites

(Pages 252–259)

Main Idea

Setting a Purpose for Reading Think about these questions as you read:

- How did the Sui and Tang dynasties reunite China?
- What religious ideas influenced China in the Middle Ages?

Reading Strategy

As you read pages 253–259 in your textbook, complete this table to show the time periods, most important rulers, and the reasons for decline of the Sui and Tang dynasties.

	Sui	Tang
Time Period		
Important Rulers		
Reasons for Decline		

Rebuilding China's Empire *(pages 253–256)*

Sequencing

As you read, place the following events in the correct order by numbering them in the spaces provided.

1. ____ Taizong rules

2. ____ The Song dynasty rules

3. ____ Yangdi builds the Grand Canal

4. ____ Wendi reunites China

5. ____ Empress Wu rules

6. ____ The Han empire ends

Terms To Know

Define or describe the following terms from this lesson.

warlord ______________________________

economy ______________________________

reform ______________________________

People To Meet

Explain why these people are important.

Wendi ______________________________

Empress Wu ______________________________

Places To Locate

Briefly describe the following place.

Korea

Academic Vocabulary

Define this academic vocabulary word from this lesson.

project

Sum It Up

How did Wendi unite China?

Buddhism Spreads to China *(pages 256–257)*

Analyzing

Why did Buddhism spread to China and what caused it to decline? After you read, complete the diagram below to analyze the cause-and-effect relationships.

Cause	Effect
	Buddhism spreads to China
	Buddhism declines in China

Terms To Know

Define or describe the following term from this lesson.

monastery

Academic Vocabulary

Define these academic vocabulary words from this lesson.

seek

medical

Places To Locate

Briefly describe the following place.

Japan

Sum It Up

Why did some Chinese people dislike Buddhism?

New Confucian Ideas *(pages 258–259)*

Evaluating

As you read, take notes on Neo-Confucianism and the scholar-officials. Use your notes to answer this question: How did Neo-Confucianism help strengthen the government?

Sum It Up

How did Confucianism change in China?

Section Wrap-up

Now that you have read the section, write the answers to the questions that were included in* Setting a Purpose for Reading *at the beginning of the lesson.

How did the Sui and Tang dynasties reunite China?

What religious ideas influenced China in the Middle Ages?

Read To Write Challenge

Civil service exams were given by the Chinese government to challenge its best students to improve government. On a separate sheet of paper, write a* persuasive essay *on whether you think their system could have been improved for better results.

Chapter 4, Section 2
Chinese Society

(Pages 260–266)

Main Idea

Setting a Purpose for Reading Think about these questions as you read:

- What new technologies developed in China?
- How did art and literature develop in the Tang and Song dynasties?

Reading Strategy

As you read pages 261–266 in your textbook, complete this chart to describe the new technologies developed in China during the Middle Ages.

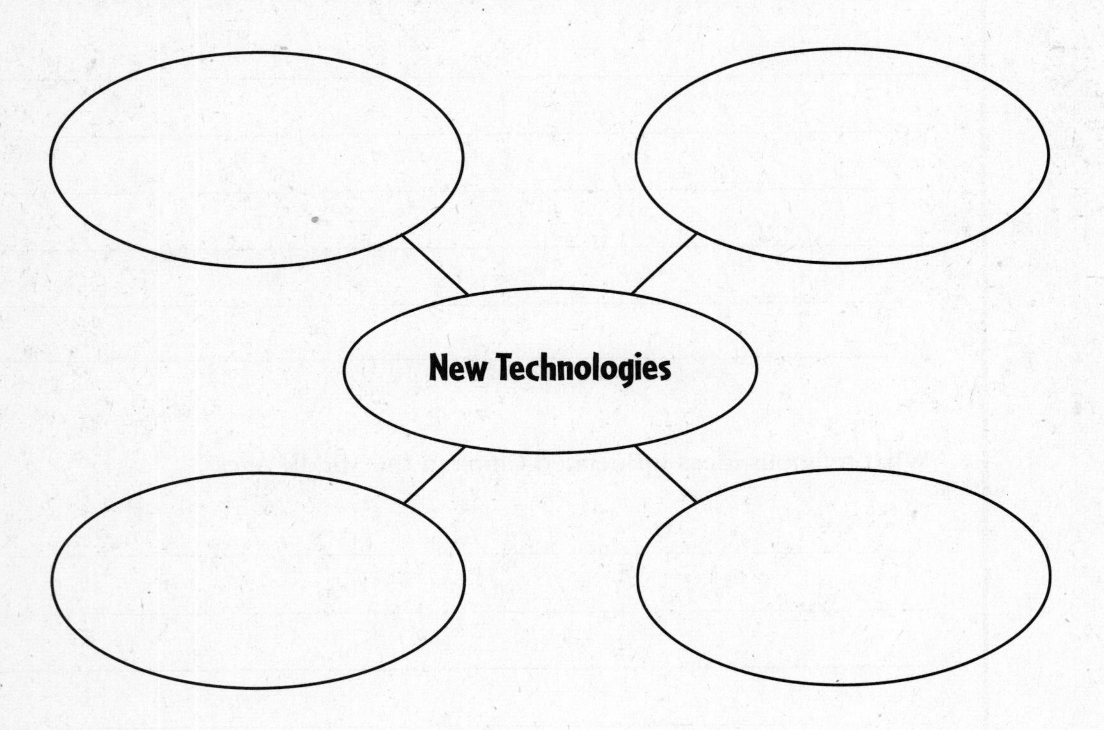

A Growing Economy *(pages 261–262)*

Determining the Main Idea

As you read, write the main idea of the passage. Review your statement when you finish reading, and revise as needed.

Terms To Know

Define or describe the following term from this lesson.

porcelain

Academic Vocabulary

Define this academic vocabulary word from this lesson.

available

Sum It Up

How did the new kinds of rice developed in China help its population grow?

New Technology *(pages 262–264)*

Inferring

As you read the passage, list the inventions and new technology that would have affected China's military. Then answer this question: How did China's inventions in the Middle Ages strengthen its dynasties?

Academic Vocabulary

Define this academic vocabulary word from this lesson.

method

Sum It Up

Why was the invention of printing so important?

Art and Literature *(pages 264–266)*

Drawing Conclusions

As you read the information about Chinese art and literature, write a general statement about each art form: poetry, painting, and porcelain.

1. Poetry

2. Painting

3. Porcelain

Terms To Know

Define or describe the following term from this lesson.

calligraphy

Places To Locate

Briefly describe the following place.

Chang'an

People To Meet

Explain why these people are important.

Li Bo

Du Fu

Sum It Up

What did Du Fu often write about?

Section Wrap-up

Now that you have read the section, write the answers to the questions that were included in* Setting a Purpose for Reading *at the beginning of the lesson.

What new technologies developed in China?

How did art and literature develop in the Tang and Song dynasties?

Read To Write Challenge

Research to learn more about one of the inventions of the Tang era. On a separate sheet of paper, write an* expository essay *about the invention describing how it is used today.

Chapter 4, Section 3
The Mongols in China
(Pages 267–273)

Main Idea

Setting a Purpose for Reading Think about these questions as you read:
- Who was Genghis Khan?
- How did Mongol rule impact China?

Reading Strategy

As you read pages 268–273 in your textbook, complete this diagram to show the accomplishments of Genghis Khan's reign.

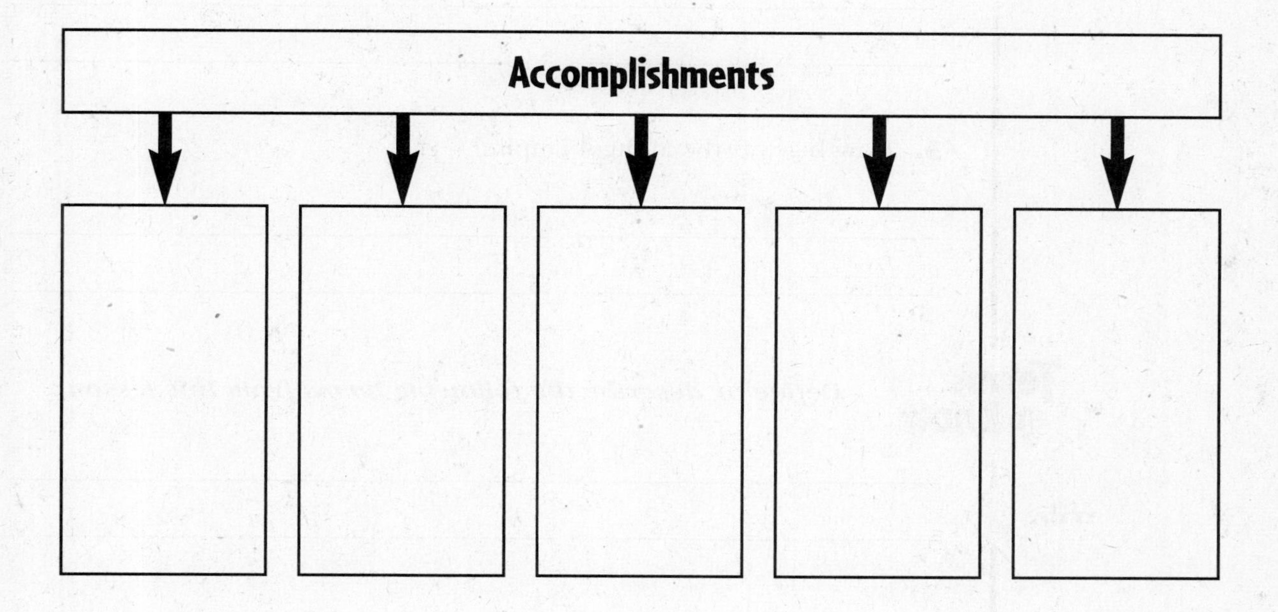

The Mongols *(pages 268–270)*

Scanning

Glance over the reading to find answers to the following questions. After you read, fill in any missing details from the passage.

1. What were the Mongols known for?

____

____

2. What were Mongol warriors known for?

____

____

3. How big was the Mongol Empire?

____

____

Terms To Know

Define or describe the following terms from this lesson.

tribe

____

____

steppe

____

____

terror

____

____

People To Meet

Explain why this person is important.

Genghis Khan

____

____

Places To Locate

Briefly describe the following places.

Mongolia

____

____

Gobi

____

____

Academic Vocabulary

Define these academic vocabulary words from this lesson.

eventual

____

____

encounter

____

____

Sum It Up

What military and economic reasons explain why the Mongols were able to build an empire so quickly?

____

____

____

____

Mongol Rule in China *(pages 272–273)*

Evaluating

As you read, take notes on the actions and effects of Mongol rule in China in the chart below. Then, based on your notes, write a short paragraph evaluating the leadership of Kublai Khan. Use specific examples from your notes to support your opinion.

Mongol Rule in China

Evaluation

____

____

____

People To Meet

Explain why each of these people is important.

Kublai Khan ______________________________

____

Marco Polo ______________________________

____

Places To Locate

Briefly describe the following places.

Karakorum ______________________________

____

Khanbaliq

Beijing

Sum It Up

Who founded the Yuan dynasty?

Section Wrap-up

Now that you have read the section, write the answers to the questions that were included in **Setting a Purpose for Reading** ***at the beginning of the lesson.***

Who was Genghis Khan?

How did Mongol rule impact China?

Read To Write Challenge

Genghis Khan and the Mongol warriors were known for their fierce and violent conquests in battle. But under Mongol rule, China reached the height of its wealth and power. On a separate sheet of paper, write three or four **descriptive paragraphs** ***about the positive effects Mongol rule had on China.***

Chapter 4, Section 4
The Ming Dynasty

(Pages 281–287)

Main Idea

Setting a Purpose for Reading Think about these questions as you read:

- How did Ming rulers make China's government strong?
- What did the Ming rulers accomplish?

Reading Strategy

As you read pages 282–287 in your textbook, complete this chart to show cause-and-effect links in China's early trade voyages.

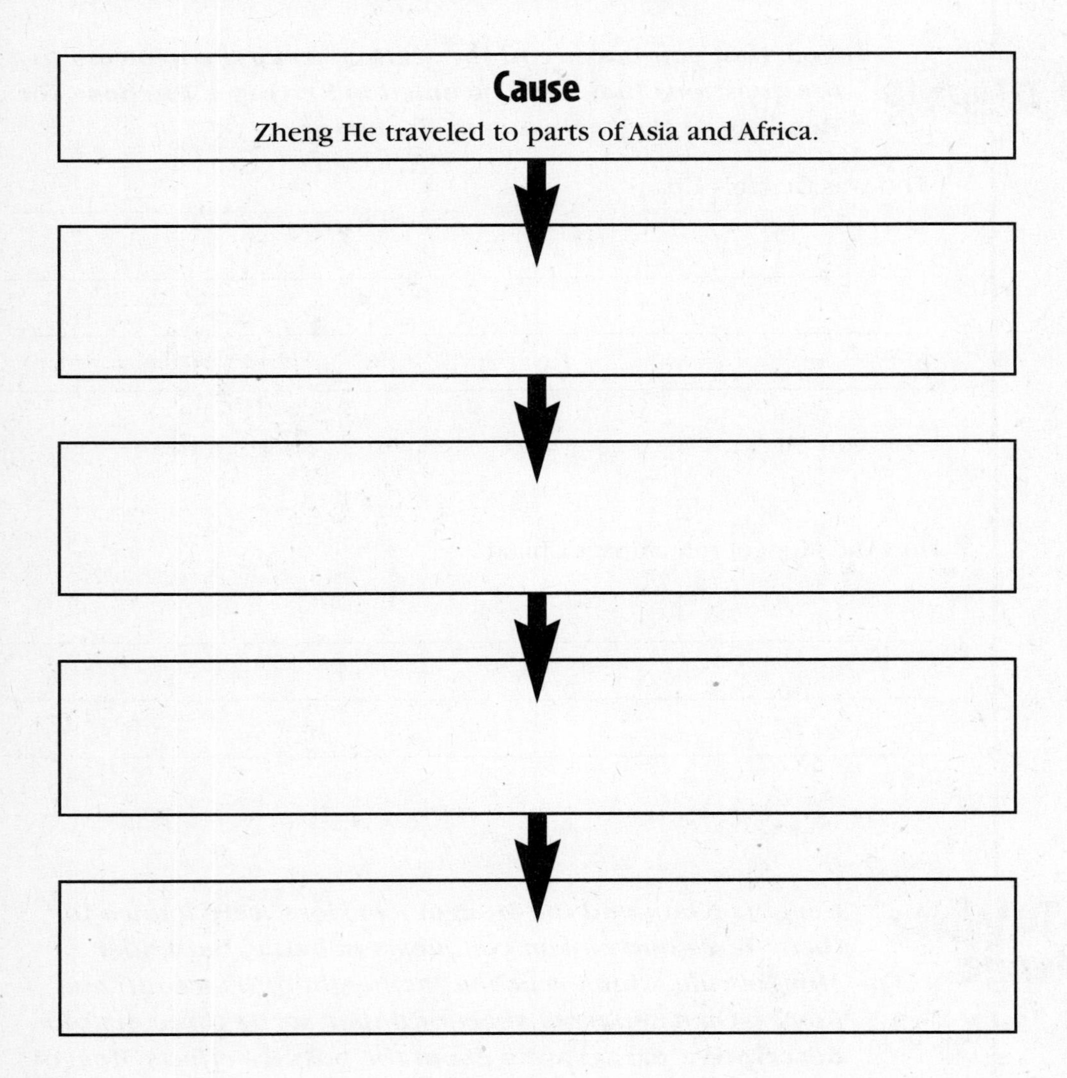

The Rise of the Ming *(pages 282–283)*

Monitoring Comprehension

As you read, list the ways the Ming reformed China in the chart below.

Ming Reforms

Terms To Know

Define or describe the following terms from this lesson.

treason

census

novel

People To Meet

Explain why these people are important.

Zhu Yuanzhang

Yong Le

Places To Locate

Briefly describe the following place.

Nanjing

Academic Vocabulary

Define these academic vocabulary words from this lesson.

erode

compile

drama

Terms To Review

Use this term that you studied earlier in a sentence that reflects the term's meaning.

reform
(Chapter 1, Section 2)

Sum It Up

What was the Forbidden City?

China Explores the World *(pages 284–287)*

Outlining

Complete this outline as you read.

I. Who Was Zheng He?

A. ________________________________

B. ________________________________

II. Where Did Zheng He Travel?

A. ________________________________

B. ________________________________

C. ________________________________

D. ________________________________

III. The Europeans Arrive in China

A. ________________________________

B. ________________________________

C. ________________________________

IV. Why Did the Ming Dynasty Fall?

A. ________________________________

B. ________________________________

Terms To Know

Define or describe the following term from this section.

barbarian ________________________________

Places To Locate

Briefly describe the following place.

Portugal ________________________________

People To Meet

Explain why this person is important.

Zheng He

Academic Vocabulary

Define this academic vocabulary word from this lesson.

contact

Sum It Up

What caused the Ming dynasty to decline and fall?

Section Wrap-up

Now that you have read the section, write the answers to the questions that were included in* Setting a Purpose for Reading *at the beginning of the lesson.

How did Ming rulers make China's government strong?

What did the Ming rulers accomplish?

Read To Write Challenge

The Ming government did not encourage contact with the outside world. On a separate sheet of paper, write an* expository essay *explaining why Ming officials resisted European trade and ideas, including conversion to Christianity.

Chapter 5, Section 1
Early Japan

(Pages 296–301)

Main Idea

Setting a Purpose for Reading Think about these questions as you read:

- How did geography affect the development of Japan?
- What ideas shaped Japan's religion and government?

Reading Strategy

As you read pages 297–301 in your textbook, complete this diagram to show the basic beliefs of the Shinto religion.

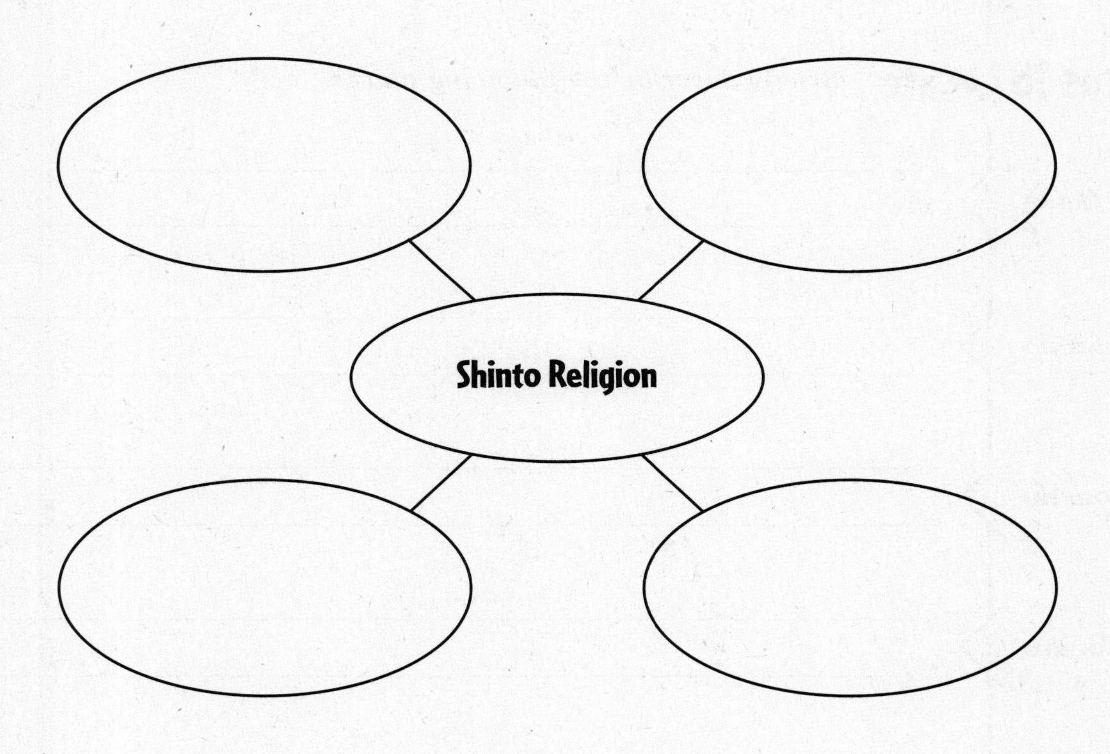

Japan's Geography *(page 297)*

Analyzing *As you read, complete the diagram below to show the effects of geography on life in Japan.*

Cause	Effect	Effect	Effect
Mountains			
Islands			

Places To Locate *Briefly describe the following places.*

Japan

Hokkaido

Honshu

Shikoku

Kyushu

Academic Vocabulary *Define this academic vocabulary word from this lesson.*

occur

Sum It Up

How did Japan's geography shape its society?

The First Settlers *(page 298)*

(page 298)

Interpreting

After you read, write a brief description of each of the people listed below. Then place names in the proper order in the diagram below to show their relationships.

Yayoi

Yamato

Jimmu

Akihito

Yayoi → → →

Key Points | Notes

Terms To Know

Define or describe the following term from this lesson.

clan

Academic Vocabulary

Define this academic vocabulary word from this lesson.

portion

People To Meet

Explain why this person is important.

Jimmu

Sum It Up

What do historians know about the rise of the Yamato?

Prince Shotoku's Reforms *(page 299)*

Determining the Main Idea

Complete the diagram below to list Prince Shotoku's reforms.

Prince Shotoku's Reforms

Terms To Know

Define or describe the following term from this lesson.

constitution

____

____

People To Meet

Explain why this person is important.

Shotoku

____

____

Sum It Up

What Chinese ideas influenced Prince Shotoku?

____

____

____

____

What Is Shinto? *(page 301)*

Summarizing

After you read, write one or two sentences summarizing the beliefs of the Shinto religion in the space below.

____

____

____

____

Terms To Know

Define or describe the following terms from this lesson.

animism

shrine

Sum It Up

How did the Japanese honor the kami?

Section Wrap-up

Now that you have read the section, write the answers to the questions that were included in* Setting a Purpose for Reading *at the beginning of the lesson.

How did geography affect the development of Japan?

What ideas shaped Japan's religion and government?

Read To Write Challenge

Reread Prince Shotoku's constitution on page 299 in your textbook. On a separate sheet of paper, rewrite the rules in your own words. Then, choose one of the rules and describe how that rule might be applied by a government official.

Chapter 5, Section 2
Shoguns and Samurai

(Pages 302–308)

Main Idea

Setting a Purpose for Reading Think about these questions as you read:

- How did Buddhism spread to Japan?
- Who were the shoguns and samurai?

Reading Strategy

As you read pages 303–308 in your textbook, complete the diagram to show the relationship between daimyo and samurai.

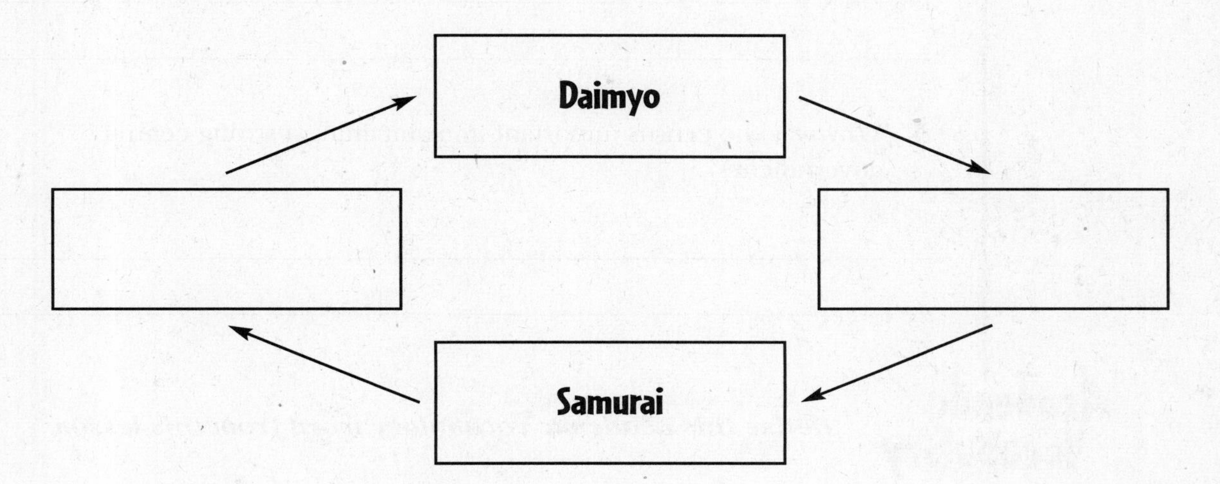

Nara Japan *(pages 303–304)*

Inferring

After you read, answer the first two questions below. Then, use your answers to these two questions to infer the answer to the third question.

1. What did Japan's census count?

____

____

2. What happened based on the results of the census?

____

____

3. Why was the census important in maintaining a strong central government?

____

____

Academic Vocabulary

Define this academic vocabulary word from this lesson.

role

____

____

Terms To Review

Use this term that you studied earlier in a sentence that reflects the term's meaning.

census
(Chapter 4, Section 4)

____

____

Sum It Up

How did Buddhist ideas affect Japan's government?

____

____

____

The Rise of the Shogun *(pages 304–306)*

Outlining ***Complete this outline as you read.***

I. The Government Weakens

A. ____

B. ____

C. ____

II. Who Were the Samurai?

A. ____

B. ____

C. ____

D. ____

III. What Is a Shogun?

A. ____

B. ____

C. ____

D. ____

IV. The Mongols Attack

A. ____

B. ____

Terms To Know

Define or describe the following terms from this lesson.

samurai

shogun

People To Meet

Explain why this person is important.

Minamoto Yoritomo

Places To Locate

Briefly describe the following places.

Heian

Kamakura

Academic Vocabulary

Define this academic vocabulary word from this lesson.

conduct

Terms To Review

Use this term that you studied earlier in a sentence that reflects the term's meaning.

clan
(Chapter 3, Section 2)

Sum It Up

Who was the shogun, and why was he important?

The Daimyo Divide Japan *(pages 307–308)*

Predicting

Read the first paragraph on page 307. Based on your reading about Japan to this point, what do you predict will happen next? Write your prediction in the space below. Now read the entire passage. Was your prediction correct? Write your reaction to the actual events in the space provided.

Prediction

Reaction

Terms To Know

Define or describe the following terms from this lesson.

daimyo

vassal

feudalism

People To Meet

Explain why this person is important.

Ashikaga Takauji

Sum It Up

Why were shoguns unable to regain control of Japan after the Onin War?

Section Wrap-up

Now that you have read the section, write the answers to the questions that were included in* Setting a Purpose for Reading *at the beginning of the lesson.

How did Buddhism spread to Japan?

Who were the shoguns and samurai?

Read To Write Challenge

Japanese rulers borrowed many efficient systems from the Chinese government. On a separate sheet of paper, write a **comparative essay** *describing the differences between the Japanese and the Chinese systems for hiring officials.*

Chapter 5, Section 3
Life in Medieval Japan

(Pages 309–315)

Main Idea

Setting a Purpose for Reading Think about these questions as you read:

- How did religion shape Japan's culture?
- What was life like for people in medieval Japan?

Reading Strategy

As you read pages 310–315 in your textbook, complete this diagram to describe the role of women in the families of medieval Japan.

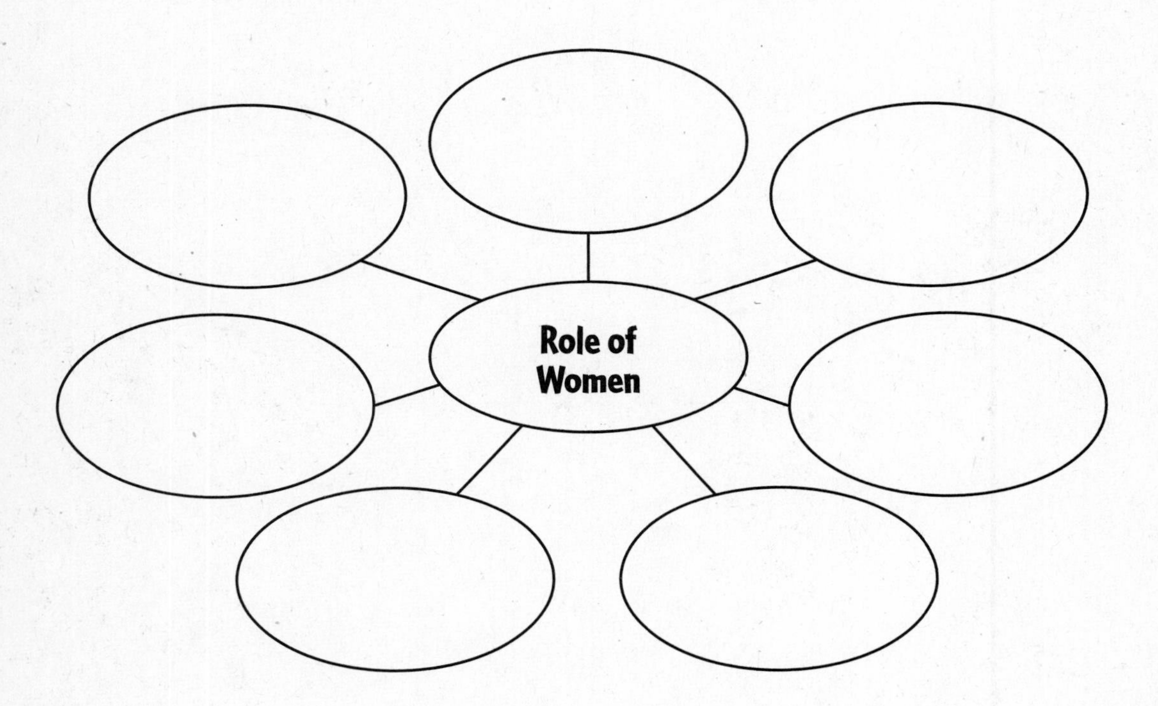

Japanese Religion and Culture *(pages 310–312)*

Analyzing

Two sects of Buddhism were important in Japan. Use the diagram below to compare and contrast these sects. What did they have in common? How were they different?

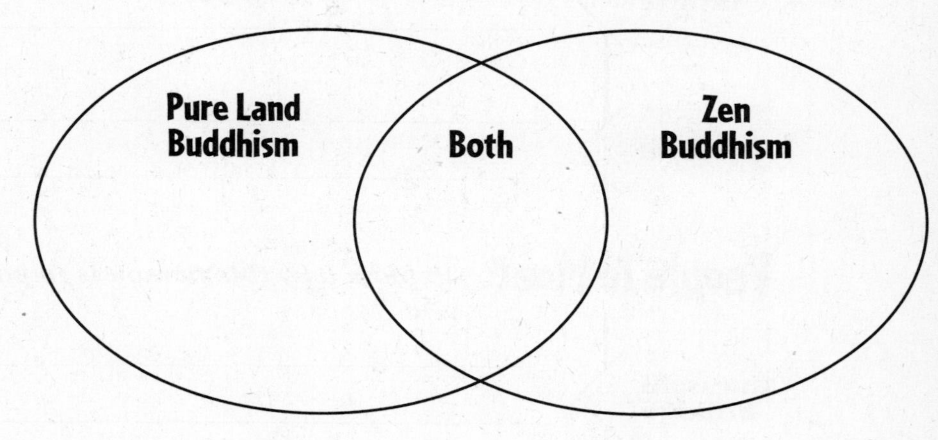

Terms To Know

Define or describe the following terms from this lesson.

sect

martial arts

meditation

calligraphy

tanka

Academic Vocabulary

Define these academic vocabulary words from this lesson.

involve

reveal

People To Meet

Explain why this person is important.

Murasaki Shikibu

Terms To Review

Use this term that you studied earlier in a sentence that reflects the term's meaning.

novel
(Chapter 4, Section 4)

Sum It Up

How are martial arts and meditation connected to Zen Buddhism's principle of self-control?

Economy and Society *(pages 314–315)*

Previewing

Preview this section to get an idea of what is ahead. First, skim the section. Then write a sentence or two explaining what you think you will learn. After you finish reading, revise your statements as necessary.

Terms To Know

Define or describe the following term from this lesson.

guild

Places To Locate

Briefly describe the following place.

Kyoto

Academic Vocabulary

Define this academic vocabulary word from this lesson.

contribute

Terms To Review

Use this term that you studied earlier in a sentence that reflects the term's meaning.

economy
(Chapter 4, Section 1)

Sum It Up

Which groups in Japan benefited from the country's wealth?

Section Wrap-up

Now that you have read the section, write the answers to the questions that were included in* Setting a Purpose for Reading *at the beginning of the lesson.

How did religion shape Japan's culture?

What was life like for people in medieval Japan?

Read To Write Challenge

Research to learn about tanka and haiku poetry. On a separate sheet of paper, write a* poem *in either style, and then describe how your poem matches that style.

Chapter 6, Section 1
The Early Middle Ages

(Pages 324–333)

Main Idea

Setting a Purpose for Reading Think about these questions as you read:

- How did geography influence where medieval Europeans settled and what they did?
- How did religion affect life in the Middle Ages?

Reading Strategy

As you read pages 325–333 in your textbook, complete this table to show the major accomplishments of medieval leaders.

Leader	Major Accomplishments

The Geography of Europe *(pages 325–326)*

Analyzing

As you read, complete the diagram below to show the effects of geography on life in medieval Europe.

Cause	Effect	Effect
Peninsula		
Seas and rivers		
Mountains		

Academic Vocabulary

Define these academic vocabulary words from this lesson.

significant

instance

enable

Sum It Up

What did Europe's seas and rivers provide for its people?

The Germanic Kingdoms *(pages 326–331)*

Previewing

Look at the following headings and write a question about each one. Find answers to your questions as you read. Revise your question if the answer is not found in the reading.

The Germanic Kingdoms

Who Were the Franks?

Who Was Charlemagne?

Europe Is Invaded

The Holy Roman Empire

Terms To Know

Define or describe the following term from this lesson.

fjord

People To Meet

Explain why each of these people is important.

Clovis

Key Points

Notes

Charles Martel

Charlemagne

Sum It Up

Who were the Vikings, and why did they raid Europe?

The Rise of the Catholic Church *(pages 331–333)*

Summarizing

What were monks' roles in medieval Europe?

Terms To Know

Define or describe the following terms from this lesson.

missionary

excommunicate

concordat

Academic Vocabulary

Define this academic vocabulary word from this lesson.

exclude

People To Meet

Explain why each of these people is important.

Gregory VII

Henry IV

Sum It Up

How did Gregory VII and Henry IV disagree?

Section Wrap-up

Now that you have read the section, write the answers to the questions that were included in* Setting a Purpose for Reading *at the beginning of the lesson.

How did geography influence where medieval Europeans settled and what they did?

How did religion affect life in the Middle Ages?

Read To Write Challenge

The Catholic Church was at the height of its power in A.D. 1198. On a separate sheet of paper, write a* persuasive essay *of two or three paragraphs predicting the response of kings to the pope's control.

Chapter 6, Section 2
Feudalism

(Pages 334–343)

Main Idea

Setting a Purpose for Reading Think about these questions as you read:
- Why did feudalism develop in Europe?
- What was life like in a feudal society?

Reading Strategy

As you read pages 335–343 in your textbook, complete this Venn diagram to show the similarities and differences between serfs and slaves.

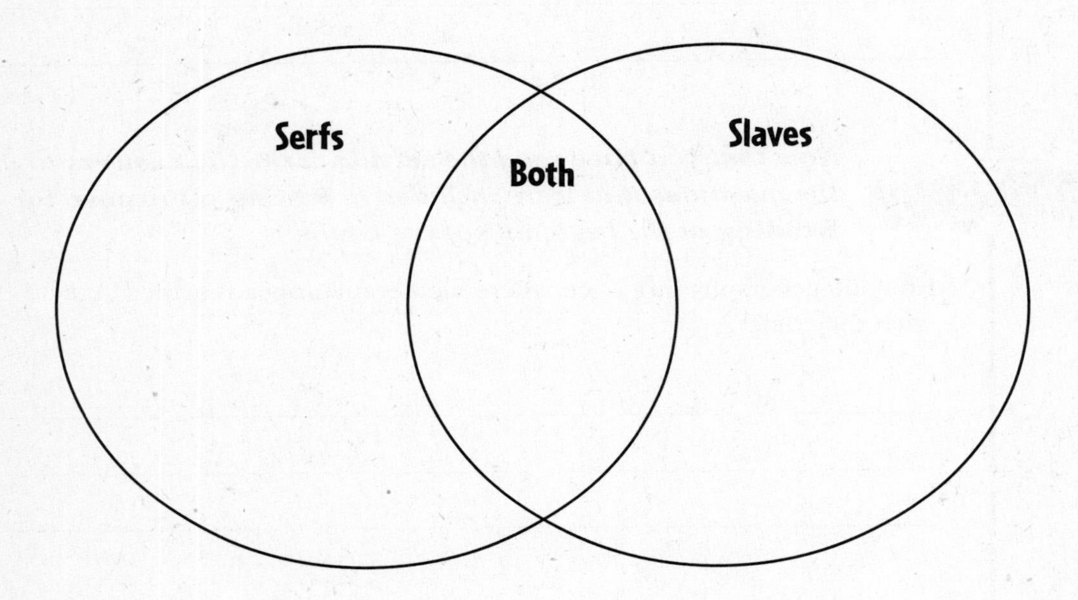

What Is Feudalism? *(pages 335–338)*

Visualizing

You live on the manor of a feudal lord in medieval Europe. Pick your role. You may be a vassal or a serf. Write an entry in your journal about the work you did today for your lord. Use details from your reading. Then add your own ideas about life in the Middle Ages.

Terms To Know

Define or describe the following terms from this lesson.

feudalism

vassal

fief

knight

serf

Academic Vocabulary

Define this academic vocabulary word from this lesson.

shift

Terms To Review

Use this term that you studied earlier in a sentence that reflects the term's meaning.

samurai
(Chapter 5, Section 2)

Sum It Up

How could a noble be both a lord and a vassal?

Life in Feudal Europe *(pages 338–340)*

Connecting

Knights followed rules of conduct. They lived by their code of chivalry. Read about the knights' code, then write your own in the space below. Include the values that are important to you.

Sum It Up

What was the code of chivalry?

Trade and Cities *(pages 340–343)*

Drawing Conclusions

Fill in the chart below to show the relationships between feudalism, new inventions, and the growth of manufacturing. Then write your answer to this question: What relationship do you see between safety and stability, technology, trade, and the economy?

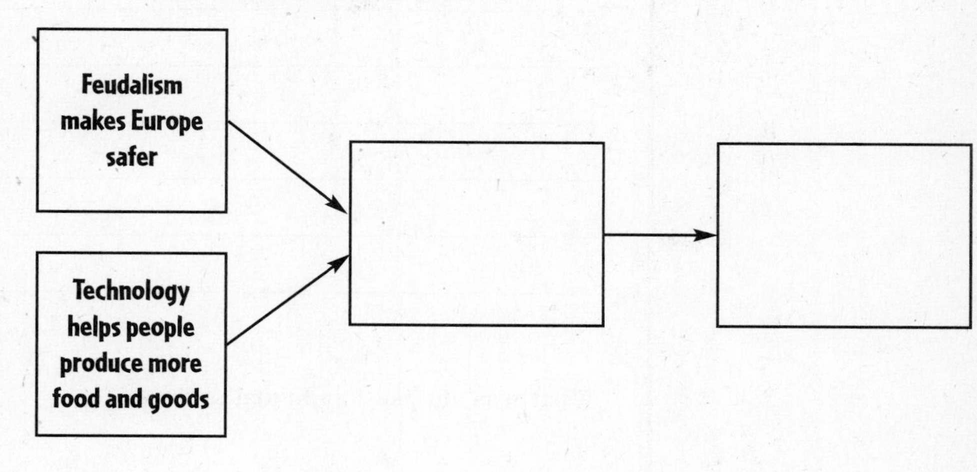

Terms To Know

Define or describe the following term from this lesson.

guild

Academic Vocabulary

Define this academic vocabulary word from this lesson.

process

Sum It Up

How did guilds change the way goods were made and sold?

Now that you have read the section, write the answers to the questions that were included in* Setting a Purpose for Reading *at the beginning of the lesson.

Why did feudalism develop in Europe?

____

____

____

____

____

____

What was life like in a feudal society?

____

____

____

____

____

____

Read To Write Challenge

Feudalism led to safer roads and increased production in farms and cities. On a separate sheet of paper, write an* expository essay *on how the shift from a barter system to a money system changed medieval Europe.

Chapter 6, Section 3
Kingdoms and Crusades

(Pages 346–354)

Main Idea

Setting a Purpose for Reading Think about these questions as you read:

- What types of governments did European kingdoms create?
- Why did European Christians launch the Crusades?

Reading Strategy

As you read pages 347–354 in your textbook, complete this diagram to show the causes and effects of the Crusades.

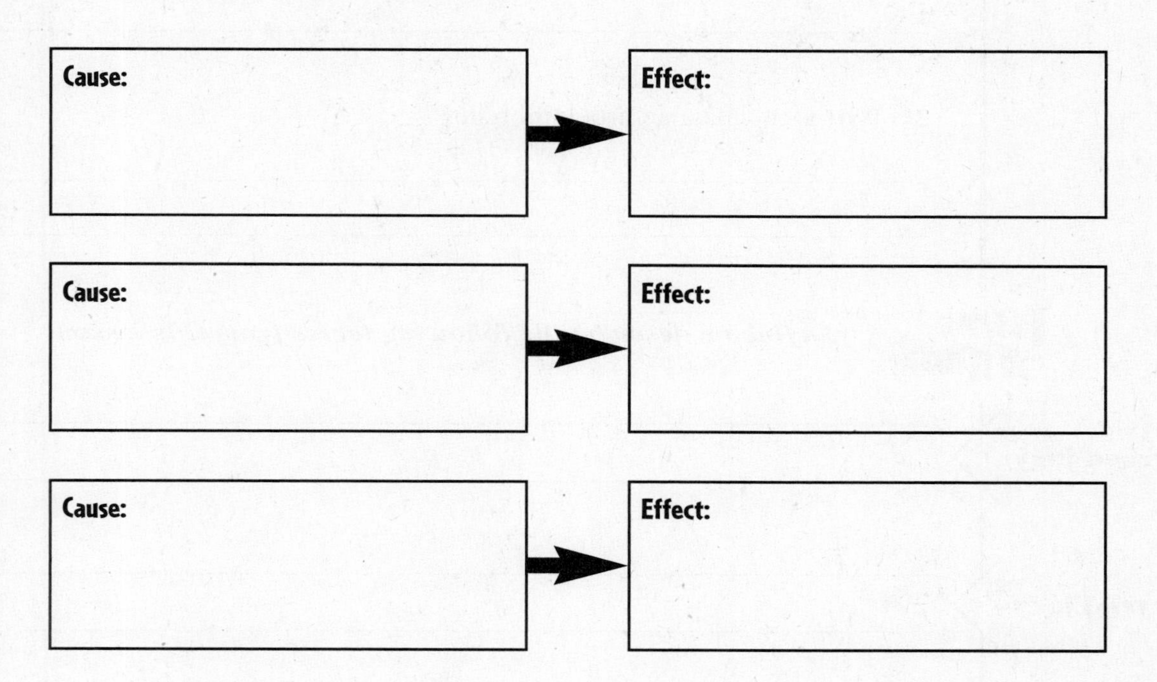

England in the Middle Ages *(pages 347–349)*

Monitoring Comprehension

As you read, answer the questions below about the Magna Carta. Review your answers to ensure you understand the document and its importance.

1. Why did the nobles force King John to sign the Magna Carta?

2. What rights were guaranteed by the Magna Carta?

3. Why is the Magna Carta important?

Terms To Know

Define or describe the following terms from this lesson.

grand jury

trial jury

People To Meet

Explain why each of these people is important.

William the Conqueror

King John

Academic Vocabulary

Define these academic vocabulary words from this lesson.

guarantee

document

Sum It Up

How did the Magna Carta affect the king's power?

The Kingdom of France *(page 350)*

Evaluating

As you read, take notes on the actions of Philip IV. Then, based on your notes, write a short paragraph evaluating his leadership. Did he deserve the name Philip the Fair? Why or why not? Use specific examples from your notes to support your opinion.

Evaluation

Terms To Know

Define or describe the following term from this lesson.

clergy

Sum It Up

How did King Philip II bring power back to French kings?

Eastern Europe and Russia *(page 351)*

Drawing Conclusions

Who do you think was the most important leader in Russia based on your reading? After you read, write a brief paragraph supporting your answer.

Academic Vocabulary

Define this academic vocabulary word from this lesson.

nonetheless

Terms To Review

Use this term that you studied earlier in a sentence that reflects the term's meaning.

missionary
(Chapter 6, Section 1)

____

____

Sum It Up

Why was Alexander Nevsky important?

____

____

____

____

The Crusades *(pages 352–354)*

Sequencing

As you read, number the following events in the correct order.

1. ____ Emperor Frederick, King Richard I, and King Philip II join to fight Saladin.

2. ____ The Crusaders create four states.

3. ____ Muslims conquer all the territory lost in the First Crusade.

4. ____ Crusaders burn and loot the Byzantine capital.

5. ____ The Muslims capture Edessa.

6. ____ The Crusaders capture Antioch and Jerusalem.

7. ____ Saladin unites the Muslims and declares war against the Christian states.

8. ____ King Richard I agrees to a truce with Saladin.

9. ____ Saladin captures Jerusalem.

Sum It Up

What did the First Crusade accomplish? What did the Third Crusade accomplish?

Section Wrap-up

Now that you have read the section, write the answers to the questions that were included in* Setting a Purpose for Reading *at the beginning of the lesson.

What types of governments did European kingdoms create?

Why did European Christians launch the Crusades?

Read To Write Challenge

Beginning in the 1100s with common law, the English developed a government that resembles today's representative government. On a separate sheet of paper, write a* comparative essay *describing elements of the English system that influenced modern democracy.

Chapter 6, Section 4
The Church and Society

(Pages 355–363)

Main Idea

Setting a Purpose for Reading Think about these questions as you read:
- What role did the Catholic Church play in medieval Europe?
- What new ideas developed in medieval Europe?

Reading Strategy

As you read pages 356–363 in your textbook, complete this Venn diagram to show the similarities and differences between Romanesque and Gothic cathedrals.

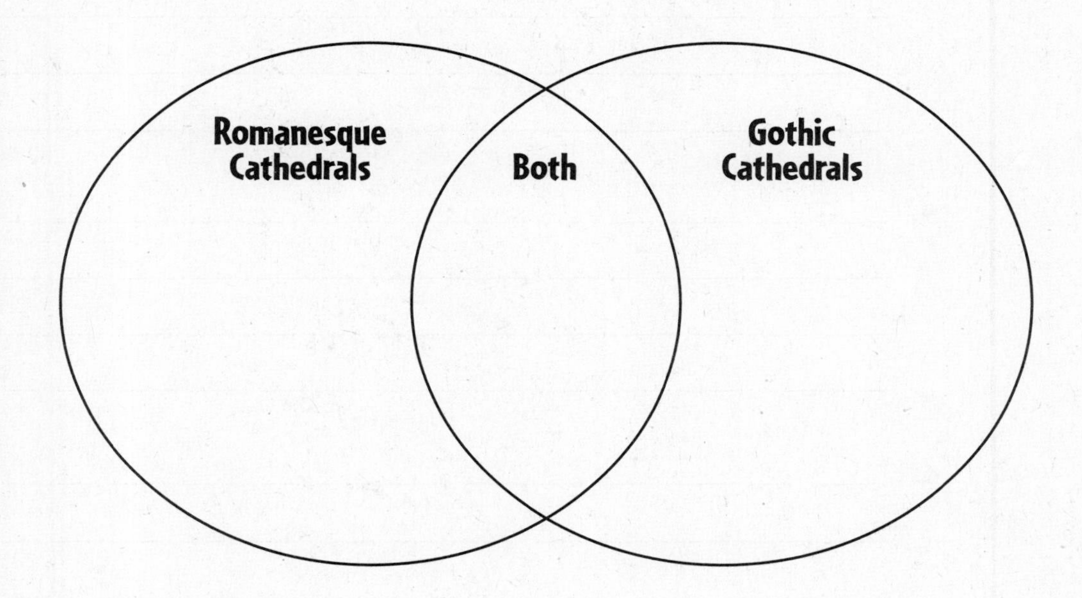

Religion and Society *(pages 356–359)*

Questioning

Before you read, scan the main headings and terms in this passage. Write four questions about the main ideas presented in the text. After you finish reading, write the answers to these questions.

1. ______________________________

____

____

____

2. ______________________________

____

____

____

3. ______________________________

____

____

____

4. ______________________________

____

____

____

Terms To Know

Define or describe the following terms from this lesson.

mass

heresy

anti-Semitism

People To Meet

Explain why this person is important.

Francis of Assisi

Academic Vocabulary

Define this academic vocabulary word from this lesson.

job

Sum It Up

How did the main goal of the Franciscans differ from the main goal of the Dominicans?

Medieval Culture *(pages 360–363)*

Determining the Main Idea

After you read each section, summarize the main idea of the section in one sentence in the space below.

1. Medieval Art and Architecture

2. The First Universities

3. Who Was Thomas Aquinas?

4. Medieval Literature

Terms To Know

Define or describe the following terms from this section.

theology

scholasticism

vernacular

People To Meet

Explain why this person is important.

Thomas Aquinas

Academic Vocabulary

Define these academic vocabulary words from this lesson.

demonstrate

obtain

Terms To Review

Use this term that you studied earlier in a sentence that reflects the term's meaning.

guild
(Chapter 6, Section 2)

Sum It Up

What is natural law?

Notes

Section Wrap-up

Now that you have read the section, write the answers to the questions that were included in* Setting a Purpose for Reading *at the beginning of the lesson.

What role did the Catholic Church play in medieval Europe?

____

____

____

____

____

____

What new ideas developed in medieval Europe?

____

____

____

____

____

____

Read To Write Challenge

The Inquisition was the Catholic Church's attempt to get rid of non-believers. On a separate sheet of paper, write a* persuasive essay *to convince Church leaders that heresy trials and persecution of Jews was wrong.

Chapter 6, Section 5
The Late Middle Ages

(Pages 364–369)

Main Idea

Setting a Purpose for Reading Think about these questions as you read:

- What was the Black Death?
- What major conflicts affected life in Europe in the late Middle Ages?

Reading Strategy

As you read pages 365–369 in your textbook, complete this table to show the path of the Black Death in Europe and Asia.

Time Period	Affected Areas
1330s	
1340s	
1350s	

Key Points

The Black Death *(pages 365–366)*

Inferring

After you read, write your answer to the following question in the space below.

How does a dramatic decrease in population affect the economy?

Terms To Know

Define or describe the following term from this lesson.

plague

Academic Vocabulary

Define this academic vocabulary word from this lesson.

approximate

Sum It Up

How many Europeans died of the plague between 1347 and 1351?

A Troubled Continent *(pages 367–369)*

Reviewing

As you read, complete the table below to summarize the conflicts in Europe in the late Middle Ages. After you read, use your table for review.

Groups in Conflict	Name of Conflict	The Cause	The Effect

Terms To Know

Define or describe the following term from this section.

Reconquista ______________________________

People To Meet

Explain why each of these people is important.

Joan of Arc ______________________________

Isabella of Castile ______________________________

Ferdinand of Aragon ______________________________

Places To Locate

Briefly describe the following places.

Crécy

____

____

Orléans

____

____

Academic Vocabulary

Define this academic vocabulary word from this lesson.

abandon

____

____

Sum It Up

What caused the Hundred Years' War?

____

____

Section Wrap-up

Now that you have read the section, write the answers to the questions that were included in* Setting a Purpose for Reading *at the beginning of the lesson.

What was the Black Death?

____

____

What major conflicts affected life in Europe in the late Middle Ages?

____

____

Read To Write Challenge

Joan of Arc convinced the leaders and soldiers of France that God was on their side in a war for freedom. On a separate sheet of paper, write a* narrative essay *from the perspective of Charles, deciding whether to support her in her efforts.

Chapter 7, Section 1

The Renaissance Begins

(Pages 384–391)

Main Idea

Setting a Purpose for Reading Think about these questions as you read:

- Why did the Renaissance begin in Europe?
- How did Italy's city-states grow wealthy?
- How did nobles of the Italian city-states make their living?

Reading Strategy

As you read pages 385–391 in your textbook, complete this chart to show the reasons Italian city-states grew wealthy.

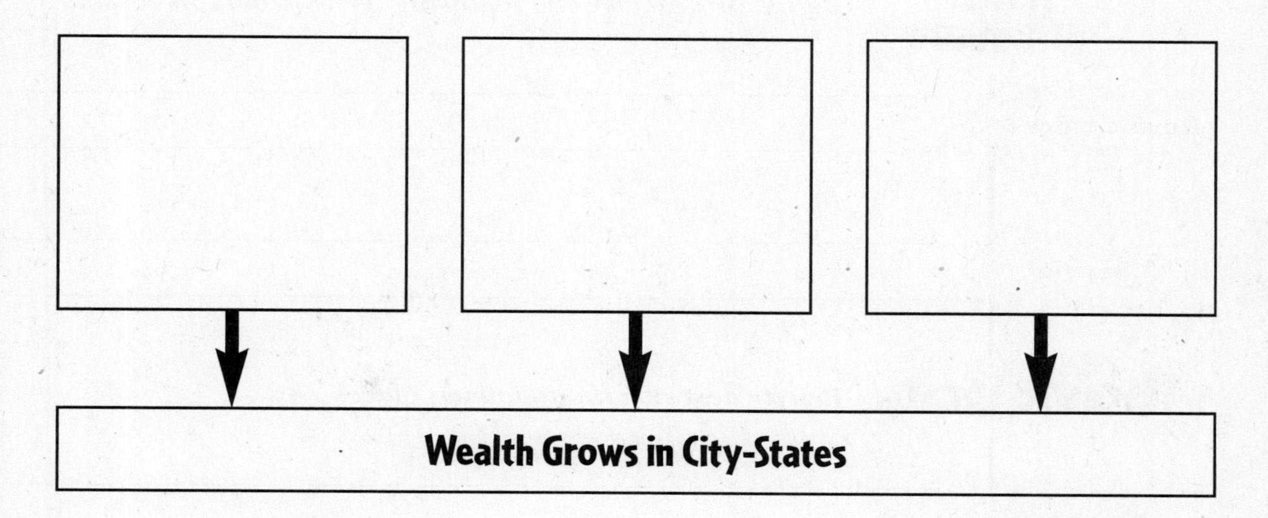

The Italian Renaissance *(pages 385–386)*

Analyzing

As you read, complete the diagram below to show the relationship between the growth of cities and the beginning of the Renaissance.

Cause	Effect/Cause	Effect
Italy's population becomes more urban	______ ______ ______	______

Terms To Know

Define or describe the following terms from this lesson.

Renaissance

secular

Places To Locate

Briefly describe the following places.

Florence

Venice

Sum It Up

Why did the Renaissance start in Italy?

The Rise of Italy's City-States *(pages 387–389)*

Previewing

Before you read, look at the headings and terms in the passage. Then write four questions. Find answers to your questions as you read. Revise your questions if the answer is not found in the reading.

1.

2.

3.

4.

People To Meet

Explain why these people are important.

Marco Polo

Medici

Academic Vocabulary

Define these academic vocabulary words from this lesson.

network

publish

Terms To Review

Use each of these terms that you studied earlier in a sentence that reflects the term's meaning.

caravan
(Chapter 2, Section 1)

Sum It Up

How did Florence and the Medici family become so wealthy?

The Urban Noble *(pages 390–391)*

Responding

What is your personal response to Machiavelli's ideas about government? Do you agree or disagree? Why or why not? Present your response to Machiavelli in a brief paragraph.

Terms To Know

Define or describe the following terms from this lesson.

doge

diplomacy

People To Meet

Explain why this person is important.

Niccolò Machiavelli

Sum It Up

How were medieval and Renaissance nobles different from each other?

Section Wrap-up

Now that you have read the section, write the answers to the questions that were included in **Setting a Purpose for Reading** *at the beginning of the lesson.*

Why did the Renaissance begin in Europe?

How did Italy's city-states grow wealthy?

How did nobles of the Italian city-states make their living?

Read To Write Challenge

Research the progression of the Renaissance through Europe. On a separate sheet of paper, create a **map, time line,** *or a* **narrative essay** *that shows where the Renaissance started, and how it spread throughout Europe.*

Chapter 7, Section 2
New Ideas and Literature

(Pages 394–400)

Main Idea

Setting a Purpose for Reading Think about these questions as you read:

- What is humanism and how did it affect the Renaissance?
- Why did literature become more popular during the Renaissance?

Reading Strategy

As you read pages 395–400, create a chart listing people who contributed to Renaissance literature.

Contributor	Role in Renaissance Literature

Renaissance Humanism *(pages 395–397)*

Summarizing

For each section of your reading, write a one-sentence summary of the main idea presented.

1. Ancient Works Become Popular

____

____

2. How Did Humanism Affect Society?

____

____

Terms To Know

Define or describe the following term from this lesson.

humanism

____

____

People To Meet

Explain why this person is important.

Leonardo da Vinci

____

____

Terms To Review

Use this term that you studied earlier in a sentence that reflects the term's meaning.

anatomy
(Chapter 1, Section 1)

____

____

Sum It Up ***How did Renaissance thinkers view ancient writings?***

Changes in Literature *(pages 397–400)*

Scanning ***Glance quickly over the reading to find answers to the following questions.***

1. What was *The Canterbury Tales* about?

2. What country was Miguel de Cervantes from?

Terms To Know ***Define or describe the following term from this lesson.***

vernacular

Places To Locate

Briefly describe the following place.

Canterbury

People To Meet

Explain why these people are important.

Dante Alighieri

Johannes Gutenberg

William Shakespeare

Academic Vocabulary

Define these academic vocabulary words from this lesson.

debate

credit

Sum It Up

What was the benefit of writing in the vernacular?

Now that you have read the section, write the answers to the questions that were included in* Setting a Purpose for Reading *at the beginning of the lesson.

What is humanism and how did it affect the Renaissance?

____

____

____

____

____

____

Why did literature become more popular during the Renaissance?

____

____

____

____

____

____

Read To Write Challenge

Research some of the inventions and ideas of Leonardo da Vinci. Then, on a separate sheet of paper, write a* narrative essay, *or create detailed sketches, describing things you think might be invented in the next two or three hundred years.

Chapter 7, Section 3
Renaissance Art

(Pages 408–413)

Main Idea

Setting a Purpose for Reading Think about these questions as you read:

- What makes Renaissance art different from previous art?
- What important method was developed by Northern Renaissance artists?

Reading Strategy

As you read pages 409–413, create a diagram like the one below to show features of Renaissance art.

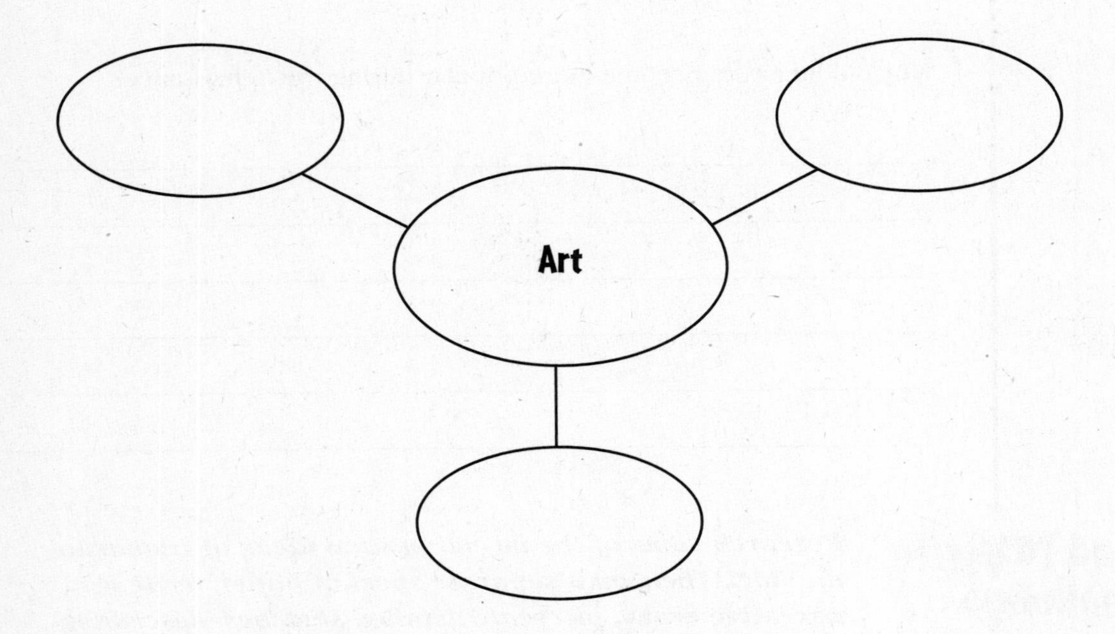

Artists in Renaissance Italy *(pages 409–411)*

Inferring

As you read the passage, take notes about the differences between medieval and Renaissance art. Then answer this question: How was Renaissance art affected by humanism?

Terms To Know

Define or describe the following terms from this lesson.

chiaroscuro

fresco

People To Meet

Explain why these people are important.

Sandro Botticelli

Raphael Sanzio

Michelangelo Buonarroti

Titian

Academic Vocabulary

Define these academic vocabulary words from this lesson.

differentiate

perspective

Sum It Up

What were some of the differences between medieval and Renaissance artists?

The Renaissance Spreads *(pages 412–413)*

Connecting

When have you seen a painting or picture, read a story, or seen a play or movie that made you feel a strong emotion? Why did you connect with that work of art? Write a brief paragraph describing the work of art and your reaction to it. Be sure to write about techniques used by the artist to make the work more real to you.

Places To Locate

Briefly describe the following place.

Flanders

People To Meet

Explain why these people are important.

Jan van Eyck

Albrecht Dürer

Terms To Review

Use this term that you studied earlier in a sentence that reflects the term's meaning.

knight
(Chapter 6, Section 2)

Sum It Up

How did the Northern Renaissance differ from the Italian Renaissance?

Section Wrap-up

Now that you have read the section, write the answers to the questions that were included in* Setting a Purpose for Reading *at the beginning of the lesson.

What makes Renaissance art different from previous art?

What important method was developed by Northern Renaissance artists?

____

____

____

____

____

Read To Write Challenge

Research elements of Renaissance art that make it unique. On a separate sheet of paper, write a* descriptive essay *that explains some of these elements in detail. If possible, include visual examples from your research.

Chapter 8, Section 1
The Reformation Begins

(Pages 422–429)

Main Idea

Setting a Purpose for Reading Think about these questions as you read:
- How did Martin Luther's ideas change the Church?
- Why did political leaders support Protestanism?

Reading Strategy

As you read pages 423–429 in your textbook, complete this diagram to show the causes of the Reformation.

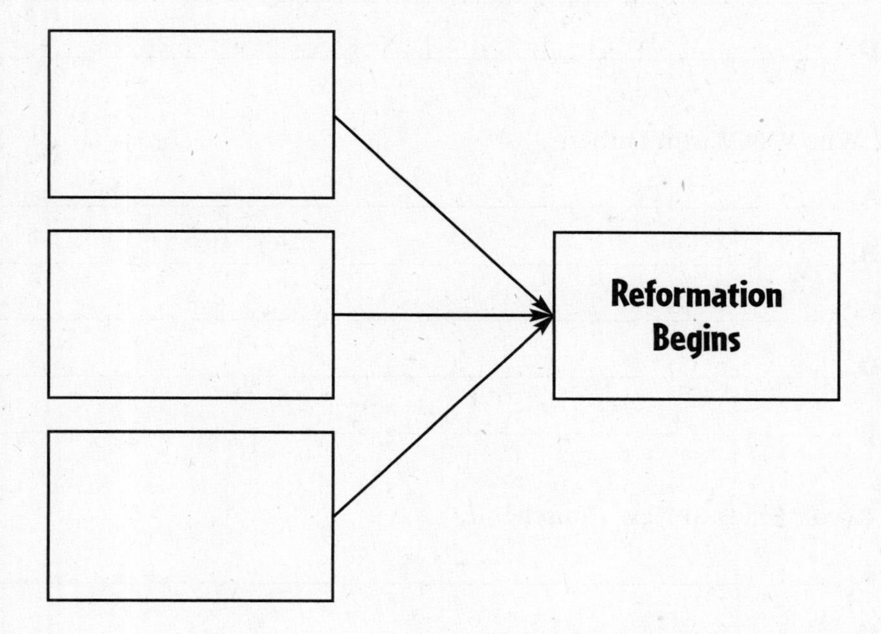

Calls for Church Reform *(pages 423–426)*

Outlining ***Complete this outline as you read.***

I. What Ideas Led to the Reformation?

A. ____________________

B. ____________________

II. The Church Upsets Reformers

A. ____________________

B. ____________________

C. ____________________

D. ____________________

III. Who Was Martin Luther?

A. ____________________

B. ____________________

C. ____________________

D. ____________________

E. ____________________

IV. Revolt Leads to New Churches

A. ____________________

B. ____________________

C. ____________________

V. Peasant Revolts

A. ____________________

B. ____________________

C. ____________________

D. ____________________

Terms To Know

Define or describe the following terms from this lesson.

Reformation

indulgence

denomination

People To Meet

Explain why these people are important.

Martin Luther

Desiderius Erasmus

John Wycliffe

William Tyndale

Places To Locate

Briefly describe the following place.

Wittenberg

Academic Vocabulary

Define this academic vocabulary word from this lesson.

conclude

Terms To Review

Use each of these terms that you studied earlier in a sentence that reflects the term's meaning.

clergy
(Chapter 6, Section 3)

excommunicate
(Chapter 6, Section 1)

Sum It Up

What was the result of the Catholic Church's decision to sell indulgences in 1517?

Politics and Lutheranism *(pages 428–429)*

Synthesizing

As you read, take notes on the reasons German rulers decided to become Lutherans. Now think about different countries and governments around the world today. Some governments favor or support specific religions. Others do not. Write a paragraph summarizing your opinion about the relationship between church and government. Use specific examples from history, from current events, and from your notes to support your opinion.

Academic Vocabulary

Define these academic vocabulary words from this lesson.

energy

resource

convert

Sum It Up

Why did many German princes support Martin Luther's ideas?

Now that you have read the section, write the answers to the questions that were included in* Setting a Purpose for Reading *at the beginning of the lesson.

How did Martin Luther's ideas change the Church?

Why did political leaders support Protestanism?

Read To Write Challenge

Luther's ideas led to revolutions in religion and politics. Research Martin Luther's life and his reasons for challenging the Roman Catholic Church. Use what you learn to write a* narrative essay *on a separate sheet of paper, answering the question of why Luther's ideas were so provocative.

Chapter 8, Section 2
The Reformation Spreads

(Pages 430–434)

Main Idea

Setting a Purpose for Reading Think about these questions as you read:
- What did John Calvin teach?
- Why did Henry VIII create the Anglican Church?

Reading Strategy

As you read pages 431–434 in your textbook, complete a table to show the major impact of rulers on the English Reformation.

Ruler	Impact

Calvin and Calvinism *(pages 431–432)*

Scanning

Glance quickly over the reading to find answers to the following questions.

1. Who was John Calvin?

____

____

2. What is Calvinism?

____

____

Terms To Know

Define or describe the following terms from this lesson.

theology ____

____

predestination ____

____

People To Meet

Explain why this person is important.

John Calvin ____

____

Places To Locate

Briefly describe the following place.

Geneva ____

____

Academic Vocabulary

Define these academic vocabulary words from this lesson.

clarify

---

consent

Sum It Up

How did Calvin's ideas differ from those of Luther?

The English Reformation *(pages 432–434)*

Predicting

Think about what you have already read about the effects of Protestantism in Europe. Now, before you read, make a prediction about what will happen in England. After you read, write your response to the actual events.

Prediction

Reaction

Terms To Know

Define or describe the following term from this section.

annul

Places To Locate

Briefly describe the following place.

London

People To Meet

Explain why each of these people is important.

Henry VIII

Mary I

Elizabeth I

Terms To Review

Use this term that you studied earlier in a sentence that reflects the term's meaning.

excommunicate
(Chapter 6, Section 1)

Sum It Up

Why did Henry VIII create the Anglican Church?

Now that you have read the section, write the answers to the questions that were included in* Setting a Purpose for Reading *at the beginning of the lesson.

What did John Calvin teach?

Why did Henry VIII create the Anglican Church?

Read To Write Challenge

On a separate sheet of paper, write a* comparative essay *that highlights similarities and differences between Luther's teachings and Calvin's teachings.

Chapter 8, Section 3
The Counter-Reformation

(Pages 435–441)

Main Idea

Setting a Purpose for Reading Think about these questions as you read:

- What was the Counter-Reformation?
- How did the Reformation allow kings to become more powerful?

Reading Strategy

As you read pages 436–441 in your textbook, complete this diagram to show the results of the Catholic Church's attempts to reform.

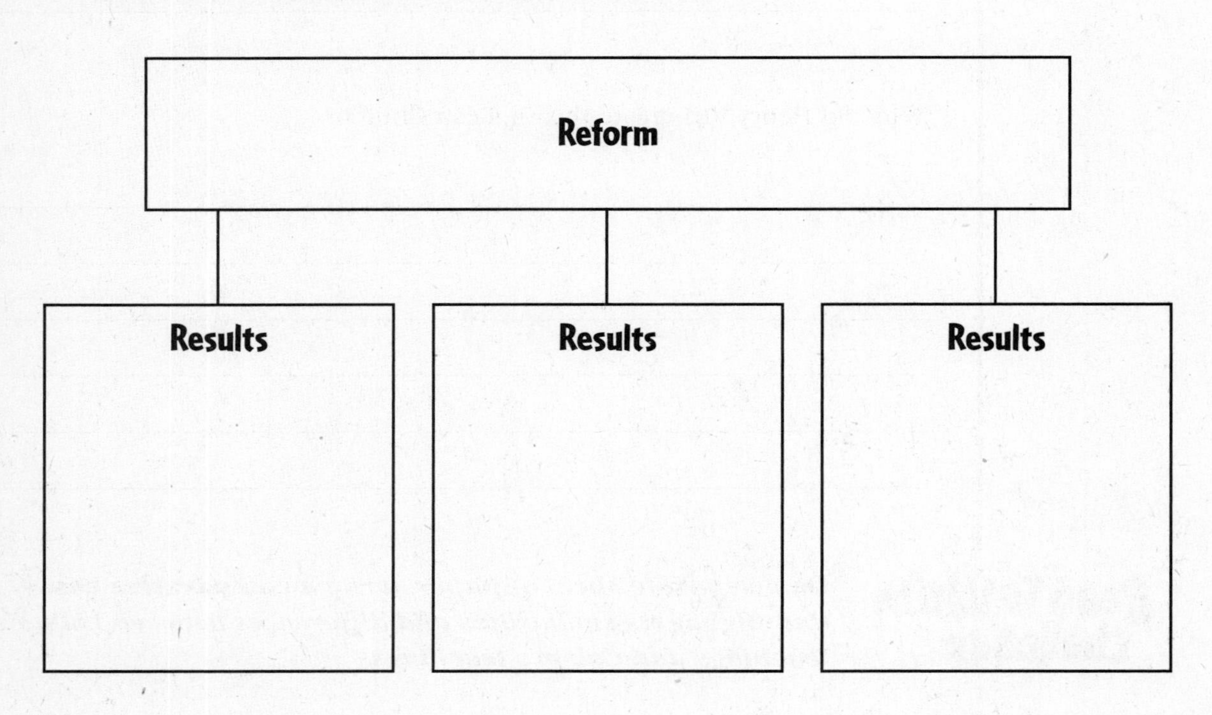

Counter-Reformation *(pages 436–440)*

Monitoring Comprehension

As you read, list the effects of the Reformation on the following kingdoms in the chart below.

France	
Bohemia	
Spain	

Terms To Know

Define or describe the following terms from this lesson.

seminary

heresy

People To Meet

Explain why each of these people is important.

Ignatius of Loyola

Huguenot

King Ferdinand

Queen Isabella

Maimonides

Key Points | Notes

Places To Locate

Briefly describe the following places.

Trent

Navarre

Paris

Academic Vocabulary

Define these academic vocabulary words from this lesson.

contradict

impact

philosophy

eliminate

Terms To Review

Use each of these terms that you studied earlier in a sentence that reflects the term's meaning.

reform (Chapter 1, Section 2)

clergy (Chapter 6, Section 3)

Sum It Up *What deal earned Henry of Navarre the French throne?*

Legacy of the Reformation *(pages 440–441)*

Drawing Conclusions *As you read, write three details about the legacy of the Reformation. Then write a general statement summarizing what you learned.*

1.

2.

3.

Terms To Know *Define or describe the following term from this lesson.*

divine right

People To Meet

Explain why this person is important.

Francis Xavier

Sum It Up

In what parts of the world did Catholic missionaries teach?

Section Wrap-up

Now that you have read the section, write the answers to the questions that were included in* Setting a Purpose for Reading *at the beginning of the lesson.

What was the Counter-Reformation?

How did the Reformation allow kings to become more powerful?

Read To Write Challenge

Research the Spanish Inquisition. On a separate sheet of paper, write an* expository essay *explaining what life was like during this terrible time.

Chapter 9, Section 1
The First Americans

(Pages 450–455)

Main Idea

Setting a Purpose for Reading Think about these questions as you read:

- Who were the first people in the Americas and how did they get there?
- What was life like for people in the first American civilizations?

Reading Strategy

As you read pages 451–455 in your textbook, complete this chart to show the characteristics of the Olmec and Moche.

	Location	Dates	Lifestyle
Olmec			
Moche			

Farming Begins in Mesoamerica *(pages 451–452)*

Analyzing

After you read, complete the chart below to identify the effects of the end of the Ice Age.

End of Ice Age

Terms To Know

Define or describe the following term from this lesson.

glacier

Places To Locate

Briefly describe the following places.

Beringia

Mesoamerica

Academic Vocabulary

Define this academic vocabulary word from this lesson.

environment

Sum It Up

How did the agricultural revolution begin in America?

Early American Civilizations *(pages 453–455)*

Drawing Conclusions

As you read, make a list of the important accomplishments of the first American civilizations. Then write a general statement that answers what these accomplishments tell you about these ancient peoples.

Civilization	Accomplishments
Olmec	
Maya	
Toltec	
Moche	
Inca	

General Statement

____

____

____

____

Terms To Know

Define or describe the following term from this lesson.

monopoly

____

____

People To Meet

Explain why these people are important.

Olmec

____

____

Maya

____

____

Toltec

Moche

Inca

Places To Locate

Briefly describe the following places.

Teotihuacán

Yucatán Peninsula

Cuzco

Academic Vocabulary

Define this academic vocabulary word from this lesson.

design

Sum It Up

What do historians think caused Teotihuacán's collapse?

Section Wrap-up

Now that you have read the section, write the answers to the questions that were included in* Setting a Purpose for Reading *at the beginning of the lesson.

Who were the first people in the Americas and how did they get there?

What was life like for people in the first American civilizations?

Read To Write Challenge

Research the early peoples of the Americas. On a separate sheet of paper, create a* map *showing where each civilization lived. If possible, locate the capital city of the civilization, and show the area under its influence or controlled by it.

Chapter 9, Section 2
Life in the Americas

(Pages 456–464)

Main Idea

Setting a Purpose for Reading Think about these questions as you read:

- What was life like in the Mayan, Incan, and Aztec cultures?
- How did the different climates and environments of North America shape Native American cultures?

Reading Strategy

As you read pages 457–464 in your textbook, complete the pyramid to show Incan social classes.

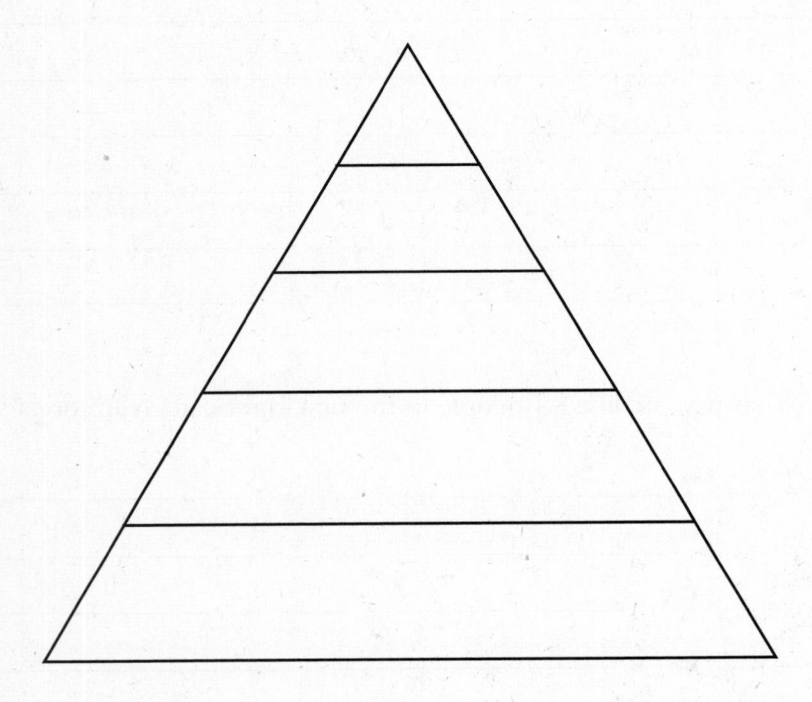

The Mayan People *(page 457)*

Scanning

Glance over the reading to find details related to the following topics. After you read, fill in any missing details from the passage.

Discovery of Mayan Civilization

Government

Terms To Know

Define or describe the following term from this lesson.

sinkhole

Academic Vocabulary

Define these academic vocabulary words from this lesson.

source

cooperate

Places To Locate

Briefly describe the following place.

Petén

Sum It Up

What was the main advantage of living in a tropical rain forest?

Mayan Culture *(page 458)*

Questioning

As you read, write three questions about the main ideas presented in this passage. After you finish reading, write the answers to your questions.

1.

2.

3.

Terms To Know

Define or describe the following term from this lesson.

alliance

People To Meet

Explain why this person is important.

Jasaw Chan K'awiil I

Sum It Up

How did the Maya treat enslaved people?

The Aztec *(pages 460–462)*

Drawing Conclusions

As you read, look for answers to the first three questions. Then use your answers to draw a conclusion about Aztec beliefs and values. Answer this question: What do these answers tell you about the Aztec?

1. What did the Aztec expect of their kings?

2. Who was worthy of an afterlife and why?

3. How was the Aztec civilization able to support such a large population?

Terms To Know

Define or describe the following term from this lesson.

codices

Places To Locate

Briefly describe the following place.

Tenochtitlán

Sum It Up

How could commoners move into the noble class?

Life in the Inca Empire *(pages 462–464)*

Determining the Main Idea

As you read, summarize the contributions of Pachacuti in one sentence. Then use the lines below to list the ideas from your reading that support this main idea.

Main Idea

____

____

Supporting Ideas

____

____

____

____

Terms To Know

Define or describe the following term from this lesson.

quipu

____

____

People To Meet

Explain why this person is important.

Pachacuti

____

____

Places To Locate

Briefly describe the following place.

Machu Picchu

____

____

Sum It Up

How did Pachacuti make sure local leaders would be loyal to him?

Section Wrap-up

Now that you have read the section, write the answers to the questions that were included in **Setting a Purpose for Reading** *at the beginning of the lesson.*

What was life like in the Mayan, Incan, and Aztec cultures?

How did the different climates and environments of North America shape Native American cultures?

Read To Write Challenge

The Aztec, Incan, and Mayan cultures all built buildings of incredible size and precision. Select any one of these cultures and research their style of building and architecture. On a separate sheet of paper, write a **descriptive essay** ***explaining the current thought on how they accomplished these amazing feats.***

Chapter 9, Section 3

The Fall of the Aztec and Inca Empires

(Pages 470–477)

Main Idea

Setting a Purpose for Reading Think about these questions as you read:

- How did Spain conquer Mexico?
- What brought an end to the Inca Empire?

Reading Strategy

As you read pages 471–477 in your textbook, complete this diagram to show the reasons Cortés was able to conquer the Aztec.

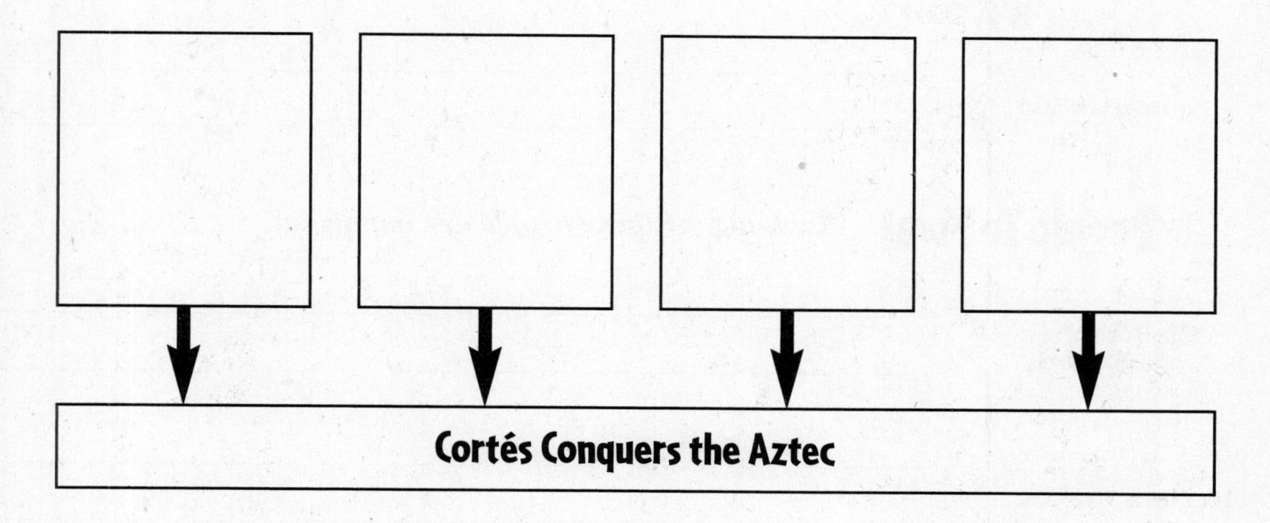

Spain Conquers Mexico *(pages 471–474)*

Visualizing

You are one of the Taino people, living on the island of Hispaniola. For you, it is a day like any other day until you see Spanish soldier-explorers approaching from the beach. Based on the passage, write a paragraph about your first encounter with the Spaniards. How do you react to them? How do they react to you?

Terms To Know

Define or describe the following term from this lesson.

conquistador

People To Meet

Explain why these people are important.

Christopher Columbus

Hernán Cortés

Montezuma II

Malintzin

Places To Locate

Briefly describe the following places.

Hispaniola

Extremadura

Academic Vocabulary

Define these academic vocabulary words from this lesson.

finance

generate

Sum It Up

Who were the conquistadors?

Pizarro Conquers the Inca *(pages 476–477)*

Analyzing

After you read, answer the question below.

Why were the Inca so easily defeated by Pizarro?

Terms To Know

Define or describe the following term from this lesson.

treason

People To Meet

Explain why this person is important.

Francisco Pizarro

Sum It Up

How did Pizarro fail to keep his promise to Atahualpa?

Section Wrap-up

Now that you have read the section, write the answers to the questions that were included in **Setting a Purpose for Reading** *at the beginning of the lesson.*

How did Spain conquer Mexico?

What brought an end to the Inca Empire?

Read To Write Challenge

Research the life of one of the conquistadors mentioned in this section. On a separate sheet of paper, write a **narrative essay** *describing this person's life.*

Chapter 10, Section 1
Europe Explores the World

(Pages 486–492)

Main Idea

Setting a Purpose for Reading Think about these questions as you read:

- What led to a new era of exploration in the 1400s?
- Which European countries explored and where?

Reading Strategy

As you read pages 487–492 in your textbook, complete this diagram to show why Europeans began to explore.

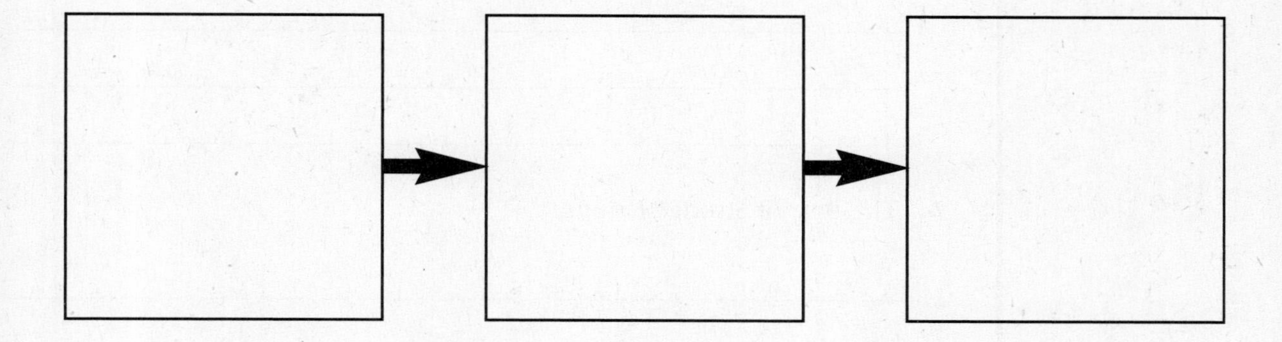

Europe Gets Ready to Explore *(pages 487–488)*

Summarizing

How did the events listed in this passage lead to exploration? As you read, write a one-sentence summary for each of the main headings to answer this question.

1. Trade with Asia

2. New Technology

3. The Rise of Strong Nations

4. Did Maps Encourage Exploration?

Terms To Know

Define or describe the following terms from this lesson.

astrolabe

compass

caravel

cartography

Academic Vocabulary

Define this academic vocabulary word from this lesson.

fund

Sum It Up

What were the main reasons the Europeans began exploring the world in the 1400s?

Exploring the World *(pages 489–492)*

Questioning

Before you read, look at the headings and terms in the passage. Then write four questions. Find answers to your questions as you read. Revise your questions if the answer is not found in the reading.

1.

2. ______________________________

3. ______________________________

4. ______________________________

Places To Locate

Briefly describe the following places.

Azores ______________________________

Madeira ______________________________

Hispaniola ______________________________

Strait of Magellan ______________________________

Newfoundland

St. Lawrence River

People To Meet

Explain why these people are important.

Vasco da Gama

Christopher Columbus

Ferdinand Magellan

John Cabot

Jacques Cartier

Academic Vocabulary

Define this academic vocabulary word from this lesson.

locate

Sum It Up

Who was the first European to sail to India? Whose crew first sailed around the world?

Section Wrap-up

Now that you have read the section, write the answers to the questions that were included in **Setting a Purpose for Reading** ***at the beginning of the lesson.***

What led to a new era of exploration in the 1400s?

Which European countries explored and where?

Read To Write Challenge

Advances in sailing technology enabled explorers to sail farther from land than ever before. Research the astrolabe or another advance mentioned in the text. On a separate sheet of paper, write an **expository essay** ***explaining how the device was used.***

Chapter 10, Section 2
Trade and Empire

(Pages 493–499)

Main Idea

Setting a Purpose for Reading Think about these questions as you read:

- How did the Spanish and the Portuguese build world empires?
- How did Europeans increase trade?

Reading Strategy

As you read pages 494–499, complete a diagram like the one below showing what led to the rise of modern capitalism.

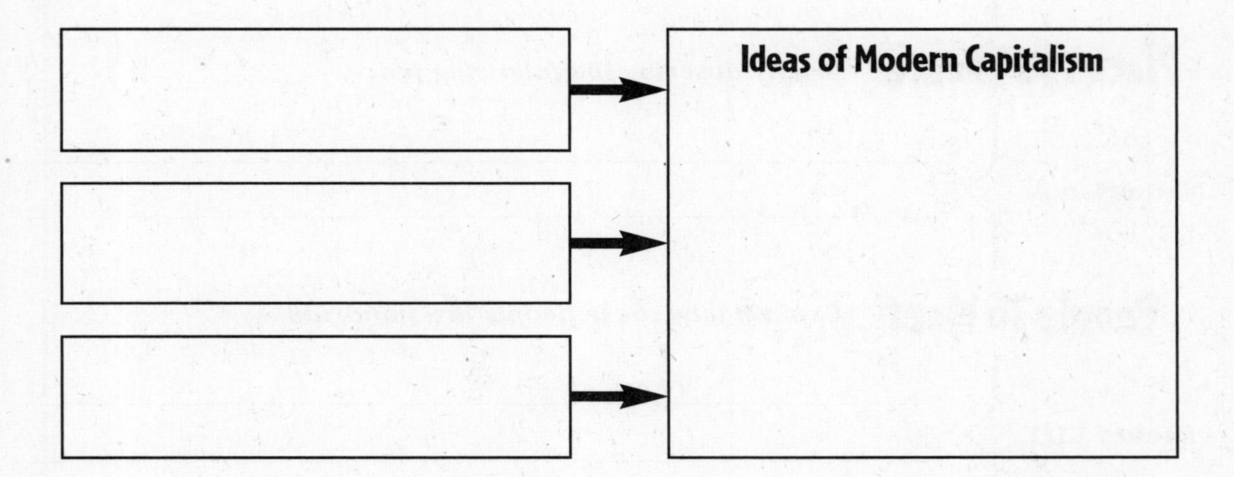

Europe's Empires *(pages 494–495)*

Determining the Main Idea

As you read, write the main idea of the passage. Review your statement when you have finished reading and revise as needed.

____

____

____

____

____

____

Places To Locate

Briefly describe the following place.

Netherlands

____

____

People To Meet

Explain why these people are important.

Henry VIII

____

____

Elizabeth I

____

____

Academic Vocabulary

Define these academic vocabulary words from this lesson.

primary

____

____

aid

____

____

Sum It Up *How did the arrival of the Spanish change the Americas?*

The Commercial Revolution *(pages 497–499)*

Analyzing *How did exploration affect European economies? After you read, complete the diagram below to analyze the effects of exploration on trade and commerce.*

Effects

Cause: European exploration

Terms To Know *Define or describe the following terms from this lesson.*

mercantilism

export

import

colony

Key Points | Notes

commerce

invest

capitalism

Places To Locate

Briefly describe the following place.

Moluccas

People To Meet

Explain why this person is important.

Pedro Alvares Cabral

Academic Vocabulary

Define this academic vocabulary word from this lesson.

anticipate

Sum It Up

How did merchants raise the money for overseas trade?

Now that you have read the section, write the answers to the questions that were included in* Setting a Purpose for Reading *at the beginning of the lesson.

How did the Spanish and the Portuguese build world empires?

How did Europeans increase trade?

Read To Write Challenge

Capitalism is the economic system still used in the United States, and in many parts of the world today. On a separate sheet of paper, write a* comparative essay *describing both the advantages and disadvantages of the capitalist system.

Chapter 10, Section 3
A Global Exchange

(Pages 502–505)

Main Idea

Setting a Purpose for Reading Think about these questions as you read:

- What did exploration and trade lead to?
- In what ways did global exchange have both a positive and a negative impact?

Reading Strategy

As you read pages 503–505, create a chart like the one below showing the positive and negative effects of the global exchange.

The Global Exchange	
Positive Effects	**Negative Effects**

The Columbian Exchange *(pages 503–504)*

Skimming

New goods from the Americas changed the lives of Europeans. Make a note of any points that support this statement. After you read, go back and fill in additional information.

Terms To Know

Define or describe the following terms from this lesson.

Columbian Exchange

pampas

Places To Locate

Briefly describe the following places.

Argentina

Great Plains

Academic Vocabulary

Define this academic vocabulary word from this lesson.

transfer

Key Points | Notes

Sum It Up

Describe the Columbian Exchange.

Problems with the Exchange (pages 504–505)

Previewing

To preview this section, first skim the section. Then write a sentence or two explaining what you think you will learn. After you finish reading, revise your statements as necessary.

Terms To Know

Define or describe the following terms from this lesson.

East India Company

Dutch East India Company

Places To Locate

Briefly describe the following place.

Caribbean

Academic Vocabulary

Define this academic vocabulary word from this lesson.

positive

Terms To Review

Use these terms that you studied earlier in a sentence that reflects the term's meaning.

shogun
(Chapter 5, Section 2)

daimyo
(Chapter 5, Section 2)

Sum It Up

How did the global exchange create problems?

Section Wrap-up

Now that you have read the section, write the answers to the questions that were included in* Setting a Purpose for Reading *at the beginning of the lesson.

What did exploration and trade lead to?

In what ways did global exchange have both a positive and a negative impact?

____

____

____

____

____

____

Read To Write Challenge

Research the East India Company and the English empire in India. On a separate sheet of paper, write an* expository essay *describing the influence of the English on India.

Chapter 11, Section 1
The Scientific Revolution

(Pages 514–523)

Main Idea

Setting a Purpose for Reading Think about these questions as you read:

- How did the Scientific Revolution change life in the 1600s?
- What is the scientific method and how did it change ideas about society?

Reading Strategy

As you read pages 515–523 in your textbook, complete this diagram to show the similarities and differences in the views of Ptolemy and Copernicus.

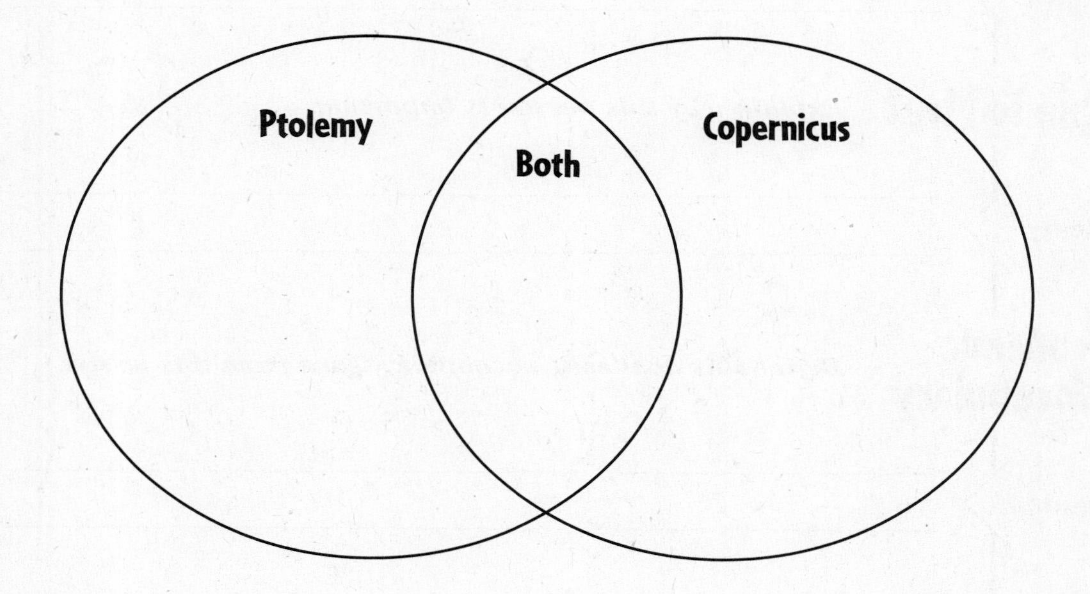

The Scientific Revolution *(pages 515–517)*

Monitoring Comprehension

What factors led to the growth of scientific knowledge in Europe? As you read, list the factors in the chart below.

Scientific Knowledge Grows in Europe

Terms To Know

Define or describe the following term from this lesson.

theory

People To Meet

Explain why this person is important.

Ptolemy

Academic Vocabulary

Define this academic vocabulary word from this lesson.

investigate

approach

Sum It Up

Describe scientific knowledge during the Middle Ages.

A Revolution in Astronomy *(pages 517–519)*

Inferring

As you read the passage, take notes on Galileo's experiments. Think about what you have read so far about the Catholic Church. Then answer this question: Why did the Catholic Church force Galileo to withdraw many of his statements?

People To Meet

Explain why these people are important.

Copernicus

Kepler

Galileo

Terms To Review

Use this term that you studied earlier in a sentence that reflects the term's meaning.

heresy
(Chapter 8, Section 3)

Sum It Up

How did Galileo support Copernicus's theory?

New Scientific Discoveries *(pages 519–520)*

Reviewing

As you read, complete the chart below to identify the major discoveries in the Scientific Revolution. Use your notes to review later.

Scientist	Discovery

People To Meet ***Explain why this person is important.***

Newton

Sum It Up ***According to Newton, what force held the planets in orbit?***

The Triumph of Reason *(pages 522–523)*

Sequencing ***Write the steps of the scientific method in the proper order in the diagram below.***

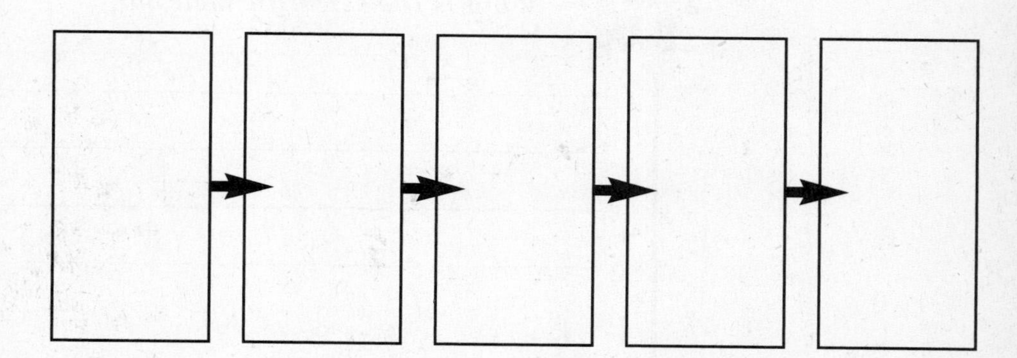

Terms To Know

Define or describe the following terms from this lesson.

rationalism

scientific method

hypothesis

People To Meet

Explain why this person is important.

Descartes

Sum It Up

What is the scientific method?

Now that you have read the section, write the answers to the questions that were included in* Setting a Purpose for Reading *at the beginning of the lesson.

How did the Scientific Revolution change life in the 1600s?

____

____

____

____

____

____

What is the scientific method and how did it change ideas about society?

____

____

____

____

____

____

Read To Write Challenge

New ideas, such as Copernicus's theory of a heliocentric universe, are often met with criticism and even hostility. Imagine that you were Copernicus and had to persuade other people that you were right. On a separate sheet of paper, write a* persuasive essay *that would help convince people of your idea.

Chapter 11, Section 2

The Ideas of the Enlightenment

(Pages 524–530)

Main Idea

Setting a Purpose for Reading Think about these questions as you read:

- What was the Enlightenment?
- How did Enlightenment ideas affect government?

Reading Strategy

As you read pages 525–530 in your textbook, complete this table to show the major ideas of Enlightenment thinkers.

Thinkers	Ideas

New Ideas About Politics *(pages 525–528)*

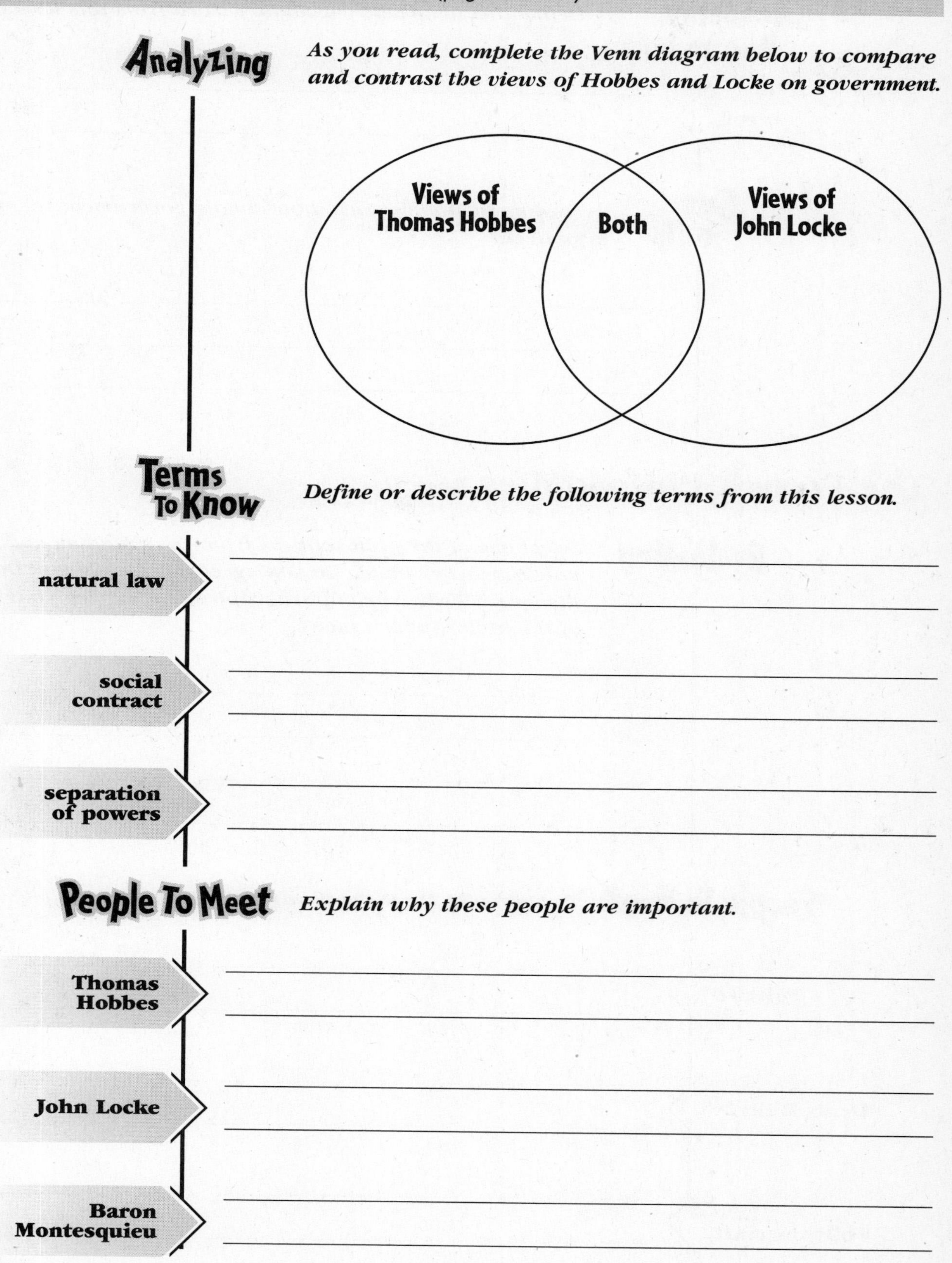

As you read, complete the Venn diagram below to compare and contrast the views of Hobbes and Locke on government.

Define or describe the following terms from this lesson.

Explain why these people are important.

Academic Vocabulary

Define this academic vocabulary word from this lesson.

error

Sum It Up

According to Montesquieu, how should government be organized?

The French Philosophes *(pages 528–530)*

Evaluating

Select one of the philosophers from your reading and evaluate his or her ideas. Do you agree with the ideas? Do you disagree? Write a brief paragraph summarizing your view of the philosopher's ideas.

People To Meet

Explain why these people are important.

Voltaire

Denis Diderot

Mary Wollstonecraft

Academic Vocabulary

Define these academic vocabulary words from this lesson.

topic

advocate

Sum It Up

Compare Voltaire's ideas to those of Rousseau.

Section Wrap-up

Now that you have read the section, write the answers to the questions that were included in* Setting a Purpose for Reading *at the beginning of the lesson.

What was the Enlightenment?

How did Enlightenment ideas affect government?

Read To Write Challenge

Many of the ideas for the Declaration of Independence and the Constitution of the United States are based on ideas expressed during the Enlightenment. On a separate sheet of paper, write an **expository essay** ***that identifies some of these key ideas and how they were influential.***

Chapter 11, Section 3
Politics and the Enlightenment

(Pages 531–541)

Main Idea

Setting a Purpose for Reading Think about these questions as you read:
- What ideas of government influenced Americans?
- Why did American colonists fight to form a new nation?
- How do Enlightenment principles influence the world today?

Reading Strategy

As you read pages 532–541 in your textbook, complete a cause-and-effect diagram showing how Enlightenment ideas led to the American Revolution and the French Revolution.

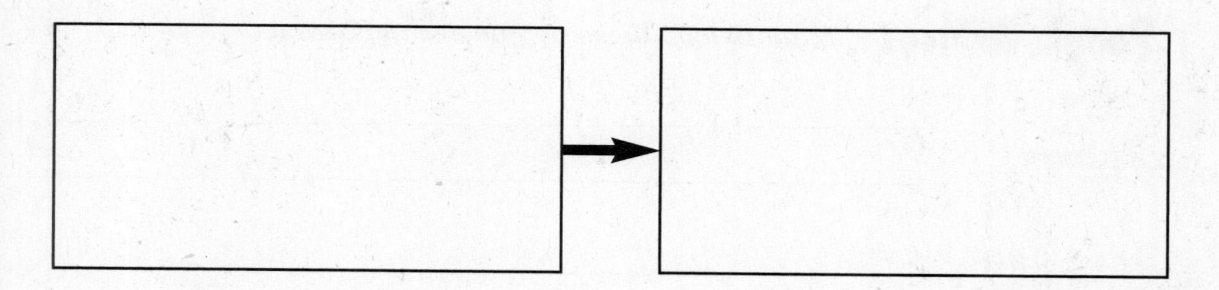

The Age of Absolutism *(pages 532–534)*

Skimming

Quickly look over the entire selection to get a general idea about the reading. Then briefly describe on the lines below what the selection is about.

____

____

____

____

Terms To Know

Define or describe the following term from this lesson.

absolutism ______________________________

____

People To Meet

Explain why these people are important.

Louis XIV ______________________________

____

Frederick II ______________________________

____

Catherine II ______________________________

____

Places To Locate

Briefly describe the following places.

Prussia ______________________________

____

Austria

St. Petersburg

Terms To Review

Use this term that you studied earlier in a sentence that reflects the term's meaning.

serf
(Chapter 6, Section 2)

Sum It Up

How did the ideas of absolute monarchs conflict with the ideas of Enlightenment thinkers?

Revolution and Enlightenment *(pages 534–539)*

Monitoring Comprehension

As you read, complete the diagram below to identify the reasons that English settlers came to North America.

Reasons English Settlers Came to America

Terms To Know

Define or describe the following terms from this lesson.

representative government

constitution

popular sovereignty

estate

bourgeoisie

People To Meet

Explain why these people are important.

George Washington

Thomas Jefferson

Academic Vocabulary

Define this academic vocabulary word from this lesson.

tension

Sum It Up

Why did the colonists decide to separate from Great Britain and create a new nation?

The Enlightenment's Legacy *(pages 539–541)*

Questioning

As you read, write three questions about the main ideas presented in this passage. After you finish reading, write the answers to your questions.

1.

2.

3.

Sum It Up

How did Martin Luther King, Jr., use Enlightenment principles?

Now that you have read the section, write the answers to the questions that were included in* Setting a Purpose for Reading *at the beginning of the lesson.

What ideas of government influenced Americans?

Why did American colonists fight to form a new nation?

How do Enlightenment principles influence the world today?

Read To Write Challenge

The ideas of the Enlightenment continue to shape our world today. On a separate sheet of paper, write an* expository essay *that examines how the Enlightenment is still influential.

Chapter 1, Section 1

Reading Strategy

Roman culture: use of arches and domes; statues portray realistic humans; Stoicism emphasized practicality and little emotion; Latin language

Greek culture: statues portray ideal beauty; Stoicism emphasized finding happiness through reason; Greek language

Both: gods and goddesses; colonnades and porches; epic poems, satires, and tragedies; recorded their own history

A Prosperous Empire

Drawing Conclusions

Student answers will vary. Students should consider the reforms made by Augustus and the strength of the military. Students should also consider the fact that the emperor did not rule alone. He held most of the power, but the Senate was still active.

Terms to Know

Pax Romana: "Roman Peace"; the long period of peace that began with Augustus and lasted until A.D. 180

People to Meet

Augustus: Rome's first emperor who ruled from 27 B.C. to A.D. 14.

Sum It Up

He built a permanent, professional army along with a special unit called the Praetorian Guard.

Roman Culture

Synthesizing

Student answers will vary. Students should use the accounts of Livy and Tacitus as models. They should apply learning from their current reading and outside learning to develop their own accounts of Roman history.

Terms to Know

vault: a curved ceiling built with rows of arches; satire: a work of literature that pokes fun at human weaknesses; ode: a poem that expresses strong emotions about life; anatomy: the study of the human body; aqueduct: long troughs used to carry water over long distances; Stoicism: for the Greeks, happiness achieved through reason; for the Romans, to hold back emotions, live in a practical way, and to accept and deal with life's problems as they come.

People to Meet

Virgil: Roman writer; author of the *Aeneid;*
Horace: Roman poet; wrote satires and odes;
Galen: Greek doctor who studied anatomy and brought many medical ideas to Rome;
Ptolemy: Scientist of the Roman Empire who studied the sky, planets, and stars; he placed Earth at the center of the universe

Academic Vocabulary

distinct: not identical; emphasis: special significance

Sum It Up

Arches, domes, and vaults added distinct style. Concrete made buildings sturdier.

Section Wrap-Up

- Augustus made Rome strong. He built a permanent, professional army, rebuilt Rome, imported grain to feed the poor, appointed governors, established a fair tax system, and reformed the legal system.
- The Romans copied Greek art, architecture, and literature. But they also developed their own ideas. They made their art more realistic. They added their own ideas to architecture and developed their own great works of literature. And they made important advances in engineering, building a huge system of roads and supplying cities with fresh water.

Read to Write Challenge

Students' expository essays should mention the Latin roots of modern languages, the use of anatomy and road systems, and influence on law, art, and literature.

Chapter 1, Section 2

Reading Strategy

Answers include:

Weak government, social problems, and economic problems
Diocletian divides the empire into four parts
Constantine moves the capital
The empire splits into the Western and Eastern Roman Empires
Attacks threaten the empire and territory is slowly lost

The Decline of Rome

Summarizing

Diocletian: divided the empire into four parts; issued rules that set prices and wages; ordered workers to remain at the same jobs until they died

Constantine: sons of workers had to follow their fathers' trades; sons of farmers had to work their fathers' land; sons of soldiers had to serve in the army; moved the capital

Terms to Know

inflation: rapidly increasing prices; happens when money loses its value; barter: to trade goods without using money; reform: political change to make things better

Places to Locate

Constantinople: the Greek city named by Constantine as the new capital of the empire

Academic Vocabulary

stable: firmly established; purchase: to buy

Sum It Up

He divided the empire into four parts; issued rules that set prices and wages; ordered workers to remain at the same jobs until they died.

Rome Falls

Scanning

1. It was split into two separate empires.
2. They were in search of warmer climates and better grazing land. They were also drawn by Rome's wealth and culture. Many were fleeing the Huns.
3. The Visigoths defeated Roman legions. Rome was forced to surrender land.
4. He was the Visigoth leader who captured Rome.
5. He was the Germanic general who overthrew the last Western emperor and ruled Rome for almost 15 years.

People to Meet

Theodosius: Roman emperor who divided the empire into the Western and Eastern Empires

Sum It Up

When Odoacer took control of Rome, overthrowing the western emperor.

The Legacy of Rome

Reviewing

Government: Ideas that all people are equal, judges are fair, and a person is innocent until proven guilty; belief that a republic is the best form of government; ideals of citizenship

Culture: alphabet and Latin language; works of Roman writers; use of concrete; architecture

Religion: spread of Christianity

Academic Vocabulary

consider: think about

Sum It Up

Government, law, citizenship, culture, language, literature, architecture, and religion

Section Wrap-Up

- Social and economic problems, including inflation, weakened the empire. Reforms were not effective, and Diocletian divided the empire into four parts. Constantine moved the capital. Finally, the empire split into the Western and Eastern Roman Empires.
- Answers should reflect that Roman ideas have affected our government, law, citizenship, culture, language, literature, architecture, and religion.

Read to Write Challenge

Expository essays should describe how Roman leaders devalued money when the economy was weak, which resulted in higher prices and less money being used.

Chapter 1, Section 3

Reading Strategy

Possible answers include:

Causes: Empire's laws were disorganized and too difficult to understand

Effect: Simplified the code and made it easier to understand; has influenced the laws of almost every country in Europe

The Rise of the Byzantines

Previewing

Student answers will vary. Answers may focus on Constantine, the location of Constantinople, or the influence of Greek culture.

Places to Locate

Black Sea: waterway that bordered Constantinople; Aegean Sea: waterway that bordered Constantinople

Sum It Up

Although Greek culture influenced the Empire, there were also many other people living in it, including Egyptians, Syrians, Arabs, Armenians, Jews, Persians, Slavs, and Turks.

Emperor Justinian

Determining the Main Idea

Sample answer: The policies and reforms of Emperor Justinian and Empress Theodora helped make the Byzantine Empire strong.

People to Meet

Justinian: emperor of the Byzantine Empire who ruled from A.D. 527 to A.D. 565; created the Justinian Code; Theodora: wife of Justinian; helped save Justinian's throne; Belisarius: general who strengthened and led the Byzantine army; Tribonian: legal scholar who headed the reform of the law code leading to the Justinian Code

Academic Vocabulary

utilize: use

Sum It Up

He conquered most of Italy and northern Africa and defeated the Persians in the east. He also reformed the laws and developed the Justinian Code.

The Byzantine Church

Summarizing

Sample answers:

The pope opposed the Byzantine emperor's decision to remove icons from the churches.

Only the Roman church recognized the pope as head of church, with both spiritual and political power.

The churches refused to help each other when attacked.

The pope made Charlemagne emperor, but the Byzantines recognized their own emperor.

Academic Vocabulary

image: picture, painting, sculpture

Sum It Up

Church and government worked together closely. The Byzantines believed their emperor represented Jesus Christ on earth. The emperor chose the leading church official. The emperor was in control, and the church leaders respected his wishes.

Byzantine Civilization

Outlining

I. The Importance of Trade
   - A. The Byzantine Empire was the center of trade between Europe and Asia.
   - B. Trade made the empire very rich.

II. Byzantine Art and Architecture
   - A. Byzantine emperors supported artists and architects.
   - B. One of Justinian's greatest achievements was building Hagia Sophia.

III. Byzantine Women
   - A. The family was the center of social life for most Byzantines.
   - B. Byzantine women gained some important rights thanks to Empress Theodora.

IV. Byzantine Education
   - A. Learning was highly respected in Byzantine culture.
   - B. Byzantine writers copied and passed on the writings of ancient Greece and Rome.

Terms to Know

mosaic: pictures made from many bits of colored glass or stone; saint: Christian holy person; regent: a person who stands in for a ruler who is too young or too ill to govern

Academic Vocabulary

stress: make important

Sum It Up

Hagia Sophia

Section Wrap-Up

- Justinian made the army stronger and reformed the law. He produced the Justinian Code.
- The Byzantines valued arts and architecture, learning and education, and religion.

Read to Write Challenge

Students' essays should argue for icons that honored Christian holy people and served as a reminder of God's presence in daily life and miracles. Arguments against icons are that icons are idol worship, forbidden by God, and banned by the emperor.

Chapter 2, Section 1

Reading Strategy

Belief: Muslims must declare that there is no God but Allah and that Muhammad is his prophet.

Prayer: Muslims must pray five times per day facing Makkah.

Charity: Muslims must give to the poor.

Fasting: Muslims must not eat from dawn to dusk during the sacred holiday of Ramadan.

Pilgrimage: Muslims must visit Makkah once during their lives.

Daily Life in Early Arabia

Responding

Student answers will vary. Students should consider both life in the desert and life as a Bedouin. They should reflect on different aspects of their life, for example, moving from place to place, dealing with sandstorms, caring for animals, living in tents, and eating fruit and nuts.

Terms to Know

oasis: a place in a desert that has water, plants, and trees; sheikh: the head of a tribe; caravan: a group of traveling merchants

People to Meet

Bedouins: Arab desert herders

Places to Locate

Makkah: richest and holiest city in Arabia; Kaaba: building in the middle of Makkah that held a great stone believed to be from heaven

Academic Vocabulary

intense: extreme in strength or degree; transport: to carry from place to place

Sum It Up

The desert, heat, and extreme weather caused people to organize into tribes, become desert herders, and live near oases or in the mountain valleys.

Muhammad: Islam's Prophet

Questioning

Student questions will vary. Generally, they should address the main ideas in the passage. Sample answers include: What was Muhammad's message? Why did people oppose Islam? How did Muhammad run his government?

Places to Locate

Madinah: "city of the prophet"; city where Muhammad established his government

Sum It Up

He preached that all people are equal and the rich should share their wealth. The poor were attracted to the message that wealth should be shared.

Islam's Teachings

Previewing

Column 1: Student answers will vary depending on their prior knowledge about Islam.

Column 2: Students should generate questions about the reading as they preview the text. Questions might include: How are Islam, Judaism, and Christianity different? What does the Quran teach? What are the Five Pillars? What is the law code?

Column 3: Students should look for answers to their questions and record any new learnings in this column.

Terms to Know
Quran: the holy book of Islam

Sum It Up
The Quran instructs Muslims about how they should live. The Sunna includes the customs based on Muhammad's words and deeds. Together, they show people how to live in all parts of daily life.

Section Wrap-Up
- The desert, heat, and extreme weather caused people to organize into tribes, become desert herders, and live near oases or in the mountain valleys.
- He taught that people were equal; the rich should share their wealth; the state should use its power to uphold religion; people should be honest, honor their parents, be kind to neighbors, and give to the poor; people should not murder, lie, or steal; people should fulfill the Five Pillars.

Read to Write Challenge
Expository essays should include the fact that the Kaaba stone in the middle of Makkah was believed to be from heaven and Muhammad started Islam in Makkah.

Chapter 2, Section 2

Reading Strategy
Good on horseback
Good with the sword
Inspired by their religion
Usually let conquered peoples practice their own religion

The Spread of Islam

Determining the Main Idea
Arabs fought and conquered other groups to spread Islam.
Sufis prayed and taught about Islam.
Merchants set up trading posts and taught Islam.

Terms to Know
caliph: the ruler(s) after Muhammad died

People to Meet
Umayyad: caliphs who expanded the empire and ruled from A.D. 661 to A.D. 750; Sufi: Muslims who prayed and taught about Islam

Places to Locate
Damascus: capital city of Arab Empire in Syria
Indonesia: country that includes more Muslims than any other nation in the world; Timbuktu: West African city that became a leading center of Muslim learning in the 1300s

Sum It Up
They set up trading posts throughout Southeast Asia and taught Islam to the people there.

Struggles Within Islam

Sequencing
2 Umayyads
1 Muhammad
4 Seljuks
5 Mogols
3 Abbasids

Terms to Know
Shiite: Islamic group that believed caliphs should descend from Ali, Muhammad's son-in-law; Sunni: Islamic group that accepted Umayyad caliphs as rightful leaders; sultan: the Seljuk ruler; "holder of power"

People to Meet
Abbasids: Islamic dynasty that followed the Umayyads; built the new capital in Baghdad

Places to Locate
Baghdad: capital of the Islamic empire built by the Abbasids located near the Tigris River

Academic Vocabulary
policy: a plan of action or guiding principle; devote: to give time or attention exclusively to an activity

Sum It Up
Shiites believe that all caliphs should be descended from Muhammad's son-in-law Ali. Sunnis accept other caliphs.

Later Muslim Empires

Reviewing

Great leader	Suleiman I	Akbar
Location	Turkey	India
Capital/center	Istanbul	Delhi
Accomplishments	Built many schools and mosques; led Ottoman armies into Europe	Peace and order to India; treated people fairly; trade increased

People to Meet
Suleiman I: Ottoman sultan who ruled in the 1500s; Moguls: Muslims who created an empire in India in the 1500s; Akbar: greatest Mogul leader

Places to Locate
Delhi: Indian city that was the center of the Mogul empire

Academic Vocabulary
style: the particular way in which something is done or expressed; impose: to force someone to comply; to dictate

Sum It Up
The Ottomans captured it, changed its name to Istanbul, and made it the center of their empire.

Section Wrap-Up
- Through preaching, conquest, and trade
- They disagreed about who should be caliph. Shiites believed that all caliphs should be descended from Muhammad's son-in-law Ali. Sunnis accepted other caliphs.

Read to Write Challenge
Students' narratives, written in the voice of Ibn Khaldun, should explain that the caliphs have the power to rule because God gave it to them.

Chapter 2, Section 3

Reading Strategy
Top: government leaders, landowners, and traders
Middle: artisans, farmers, and workers
Bottom: enslaved people

Trade and Everyday Life

Inferring
Generally, students should consider how a common language and common currency would make it easier to trade. Merchants could communicate easily with people in other countries, and they could make business deals more easily with coins.

Terms to Know
mosque: a Muslim house of worship; bazaar: a marketplace

Academic Vocabulary
widespread: covering a large area; common

Sum It Up
They gave them coins.

Muslim Achievements

Scanning
Possible answers include:
Math and science: algebra; Arabic numerals; perfected the Greek astrolabe; founders of chemistry; system for categorizing substances as animal, vegetable, and mineral; identified diseases; discovered blood circulates
Writing: Quran; *The Arabian Nights; Rubaiyat;* history
Art and buildings: art form based on Islam; mosques; minarets; Alhambra; Taj Mahal

Terms to Know
minaret: tower on a mosque; crier: a person who calls Muslims to prayer five times a day

Academic Vocabulary
innovate: to do something a new way

People to Meet
Mamun: Abbasid caliph who founded the House of Wisdom in Baghdad; al-Razi: famous Muslim chemist; developed a system for categorizing substances by animal, mineral, or vegetable; Ibn Sina: Persian doctor who showed how diseases spread from person to person; Omar Khayyam: Persian poet who wrote the *Rubaiyat;* Ibn Khaldun: great Muslim historian; wrote that all civilizations rise, grow, and then fall

Places to Locate
Granada: location in Spain of the most famous Muslim palace, Alhambra; Agra: location in India of the Taj Mahal

Sum It Up

Algebra; Arabic numerals; perfected the Greek astrolabe; founders of chemistry; system for categorizing substances as animal, vegetable, and mineral; identified diseases; discovered blood circulates

Section Wrap-Up

- Muslims traded very successfully. Cities grew, but most people lived in villages in the country. Society was divided, with government leaders, landowners, and traders at the top; artisans, farmers, and workers in the middle; and enslaved people at the bottom.
- Math and science: algebra; Arabic numerals; perfected the Greek astrolabe; founders of chemistry; system for categorizing as animal, vegetable, and mineral; identified diseases; discovered blood circulates; spread of disease
  Culture: Quran; *The Arabian Nights; Rubaiyat;* history; art form based on Islam; mosques; minarets; Alhambra; Taj Mahal

Read to Write Challenge

Students' comparative essays should describe the Byzantine's use of icons compared to the Muslim rule against making images of Muhammad and his life in Muslim art.

Chapter 3, Section 1

Reading Strategy

Ghana: taxes on trade; iron weapons; huge army; salt and gold

Mali: seized capital of Ghana; won control of land from Atlantic coast to Timbuktu; control of gold-mining areas; rebuilt gold and salt trade

Songhai: drove out the Berbers; seized control of river trade; took over Berber salt mines; built largest empire in West Africa

Rain Forest: sculpture and carving; surplus food; kept other empires from expanding past its dense forests

East Africa: Islam and Christianity grow; Indian Ocean and Arab trade routes

Africa's Geography

Summarizing

Tropics: In this area, open grasslands with high temperatures and uneven rains are good for herding animals.
Deserts: The deserts of Africa include the Sahara and the Kalamari.
Rain Forests: hot, steamy areas along the Equator
Sea Coasts: mild climate along the Mediterranean Sea where crops can be grown

Terms to Know

plateau: an area of high flat land

Terms to Review

Sample sentence:
Desert travelers must look for oases to find water, plants, and trees.

Sum It Up

The rich soil along the Niger River grows many crops. Many civilizations were established and united by trade along the River.

African Trading Empires

Questioning

Student questions will vary. Generally, they should address the main ideas in the passage. Sample answers include: How did the empire of Ghana grow rich? How did the empire of Mali grow? What brought the empire of Songhai to an end?

Terms to Know

griot: a storyteller; dhow: a sailboat

Academic Vocabulary

fee: money paid for a service; diminish: to become less or smaller; prime: to be of highest quality or importance

People to Meet

Sundiata Keita: warrior-king who took over Ghana and ruled Mali; "Lion Prince"; Mansa Musa: last strong king of Mali; Sunni Ali: leader of Songhai Empire who drove out the Berbers; built the largest empire in West Africa

Places to Locate

Benue River: river in present-day Nigeria where the Bantu lived; Ghana: first African empire that rose to power in the A.D. 400s; Mali: African empire that rose to power in the 1200s; Timbuktu: African trading city that was part of Mali; Songhai: African empire that rose to power in 1468; largest empire in West Africa; Axum: powerful city-state in East Africa

Sum It Up

West Africa had deposits of salt and gold.

Section Wrap-Up

- The natural resources of West Africa led to kingdoms based on trade. Rain forest kingdoms produced a surplus of food because of the fertile soil. This food could also be traded. Eastern city-states served as centers of trade because they were located on important waterways.
- Trade brought wealth and different cultures. Salt and gold were the most valuable trading items.

Read to Write Challenge

Persuasive essays should list common skills, such as pottery, mining, and iron working, as well as the common roots of many African languages and traditions that were introduced by the Bantu.

Chapter 3, Section 2

Reading Strategy

Box 1: African influences
Box 2: Muslim influences—Arab and Persia settlers

Traditional African Religions

Drawing Conclusions

Practices: Belief in one supreme god who is the creator; talk directly with their god; talk through lesser gods; ancestors' spirits stayed in the community and helped them talk with their god
Conclusions will vary. Generally, students should think about the importance of religious beliefs to culture. They were a very big part of the people's lives. And they helped people connect with their ancestors. These practices provided rules for living and helped people stay in touch with their history.

People to Meet

Olaudah Equiano: member of the Igbo who wrote about the African belief in one creator

Academic Vocabulary

vary: to be different

Sum It Up

They stayed in the community after they died and helped people talk with the supreme god or solve problems.

Islam in Africa

Analyzing

Mansa Musa: built mosques in Mali; set up Muslim libraries in Timbuktu; journeyed to Makkah and brought back Islamic teachers, architects, and writers; Askia Muhammad: required local courts to honor Muslim law; had Timbuktu's university become an important Islamic center of learning; set up 150 schools to teach the Quran

Terms to Know

sultan: a leader; Swahili: language and culture of people from the East African coast

People to Meet

Ibn Battuta: Arab lawyer who journeyed through the Muslim world for almost 30 years; Askia Muhammad: general who took over the Songhai government and built the largest empire in medieval West Africa

Places to Locate

Makkah: Muslim holy city

Academic Vocabulary

accompany: to travel with someone or something; element: a part of a larger whole

Terms to Review

Sample sentences:
Muslims follow the teaching of their holy book, the Quran.
Mansa Musa built many mosques for Muslim worship.

Sum It Up
He declared himself king and fought with the support of the Muslim townspeople to drive Sunni Ali's family out of Songhai.

Government and Society

Visualizing
Student answers will vary. Paragraphs should build on the images from the passage to create a visual picture of a meeting with the king. Images from the text include the royal courtyard, the silk tent, the king's cap of gold and jewel-covered robe, royal officials, guard dogs, and bowing.

Terms to Know
clan: a group of people descended from the same ancestor

Academic Vocabulary
benefit: to receive help from

Sum It Up
Mali was bigger, so royal officials had more responsibility. Generals were in charge of the provinces.

Section Wrap-Up
- Islam, Christianity, and African beliefs all influenced the culture. Muslim influences came from Arab and Persian traders.
- Kings settled arguments, managed trade, and protected the empire. The most successful states set up some type of central authority and divided the empire into provinces.

Read to Write Challenge
Students' narratives should include the trade advantages for a ruler who practiced the same religion as his merchants. Students may also infer the advantages in sharing religion with potential invaders or slave traders.

Chapter 3, Section 3

Reading Strategy
Enslavement in Africa: criminals and enemies were enslaved; staying in Africa meant hope of escape; could win or buy their freedom
Enslavement in Europe: taken to other lands; no hope of escape or freedom
Both: worked as laborers; did not receive pay for their work; were captives as a result of raids on their villages.

Life in Medieval Africa

Connecting
Student answers will vary. Students should write about a story passed down in their family or larger community. They should reflect on the story and how it has impacted their own history and relationships.

Terms to Know
extended family: a family made up of many generations; matrilineal: the practice of tracing a family through the mother rather than the father; oral history: stories told to pass on history from generation to generation

People to Meet
Dahia al-Kahina: African queen who led the fight against the Muslim invasion of her kingdom in the A.D. 600s; Nzinga: African queen who ruled lands in present-day Angola and Congo

Academic Vocabulary
bond: connection, link

Terms to Review
Sample sentence:
African griots passed down stories and lessons about living.

Sum It Up
Lived in extended families and were matrilineal.

Slavery

Previewing
Student answers will vary. Answers may focus on the slave trade in Africa and the slave trade in Europe.

Academic Vocabulary
release: set free

Sum It Up
After exploration, the slave trade increased rapidly as a result of Europe's desire for free labor to plant and harvest crops in the new lands they settled.

African Culture

Synthesizing
Student answers will vary. Students should make connections between the types of music, art, stories, and dance in their reading and in the world around them today.

Sum It Up
They believed that dance allowed the spirits to express themselves.

Section Wrap-Up
- The development and growth of trade, the spread of Islam, and the growth of the slave trade shaped the culture of medieval Africa.
- African religious beliefs, art, stories, music, dress, names, and dance all affect cultures around the world today.

Read to Write Challenge
Students' expository essays should describe how captives were sold into slavery in Europe or Arabia for profit. Enslaved Africans in Africa previously had some hope of change or escape.

Chapter 4, Section 1

Reading Strategy
Sui: A.D. 581–A.D. 618; Wendi and Yangdi; people revolted under high taxes
Tang: A.D. 618–A.D. 907; Taizong and Empress Wu; nomads took control of the Silk Road and weakened the economy; revolts and disorder

Rebuilding China's Empire

Sequencing
4 Taizong rules
6 The Song dynasty rules
3 Yangdi builds the Grand Canal
2 Wendi reunites China
5 Empress Wu rules
1 The Han empire ends

Terms to Know
warlord: military leader who runs a government; economy: system that includes the ways people produce, sell, and buy things; reform: a change that make things better, an improvement

People to Meet
Wendi: general who reunited China; became emperor and founded the Sui dynasty; Empress Wu: woman who became empress of China; the only woman to rule the country on her own

Places to Locate
Korea: country located northeast of China; broke away from China to build its own civilization

Academic Vocabulary
project: plan; job

Sum It Up
Wendi declared himself emperor and won many battles. He founded a new dynasty called the Sui.

Buddhism Spreads to China

Analyzing
1. Traders and missionaries bring Buddhism to China; many Chinese are seeking relief from suffering
2. Tang officials feared Buddhism's growing power; the Tang destroyed monasteries and temples

Terms to Know
monastery: a place where nuns and monks live in a religious community

Academic Vocabulary
seek: to look for; medical: health care

Places to Locate
Japan: islands near China; place where Buddhism won many followers

Sum It Up
They thought it was wrong for temples and monasteries to accept donations; they believed monks and nuns weakened respect for families; officials feared Buddhism's growing power

New Confucian Ideas

Evaluating
Student answers should note the following facts: the Song and Tang dynasties supported Neo-Confucianism. Their civil-service exams tested for knowledge of Confucian writings. Only those who passed on the first try could get government jobs. This resulted in a new class of scholar-officials based on merit.

Sum It Up
Confucianism picked up some Buddhist and Daoist beliefs; it became more than a system of rules for being good; it became a religion that promised peace of mind and harmony with nature.

Section Wrap-Up
- They fought many battles and founded new dynasties. They rebuilt China and strengthened the government with reforms.
- Buddhism spread to China. Neo-Confucianism won many followers.

Read to Write Challenge
Persuasive essays should include ideas for relieving the stress and burden placed on candidates; ways to include students other than the wealthy in testing.

Chapter 4, Section 2

Reading Strategy
Coal and steel
Printing and movable type
Gunpowder
Rudders
Compass

A Growing Economy

Determining the Main Idea
The Tang dynasty strengthened China's economy by supporting farming and trade.

Terms to Know
porcelain: material made from fine clay and baked at high temperatures

Academic Vocabulary
available: obtainable, ready for use

Sum It Up
The new rice could grow in poor soil, produce more per acre, grow faster, and resist disease. Farmers could grow more rice so people had more food to eat.

New Technology

Inferring
New Technology: steel, gunpowder, fire lance, rudders and sails, compass
Effects: stronger weapons would have meant a stronger military, which would have strengthened the dynasties; the ability to sail farther could have resulted in a navy

Academic Vocabulary
method: a particular way of doing something

Sum It Up
More books could be made, and ideas could spread more rapidly. Printing paper money helped the economy to expand and cities to grow.

Art and Literature

Drawing Conclusions
Student conclusions should be based on their reading. Answers will vary. Generally, students should consider what each art form conveys about the culture, the people, or the artists.

Terms to Know
calligraphy: the art of fine handwriting

Places to Locate
Chang'an: capital city during the Tang and Song dynasties; home to many artists and poets during the golden age

People to Meet
Li Bo: popular poet during the Tang era; often wrote about nature; Du Fu: popular poet during the Tang era; often wrote about social injustice

Sum It Up
He wrote about social injustice and the problems of the poor.

Section Wrap-Up
- Coal and steel; printing and movable type; gunpowder; rudders; compass
- These eras were a golden age for Chinese culture. Rulers actively supported art and literature. Poetry, painting, and porcelain all developed as art forms during this period.

Read to Write Challenge
Students will choose an invention from the Tang era, such as paper currency, the compass, rudder, sail, or gunpowder, and list its uses today.

Chapter 4, Section 3

Reading Strategy
United the Mongol tribes
Brought together Mongol laws in a new code
Created a group of tribal chiefs to help him plan military campaigns
Gathered an army of more than 100,000 warriors
Conquered other people on the steppes and all of northern China

The Mongols

Scanning
1. Ability to ride horses and ability to wage war
2. Cruelty and use of terror
3. From the Pacific Ocean in the east to Eastern Europe in the west, and from Siberia in the north to the Himalaya in the south

Terms to Know
tribe: a loosely organized group of related families or people of the same culture; steppe: wide rolling grassy land that stretches from the Black Sea to northern China; terror: actions that cause fear or scare people

People to Meet
Genghis Khan: leader who united the Mongols; literally means "strong ruler."

Places to Locate
Mongolia: land north of China; home of the Mongols; Gobi: vast desert that covers parts of Mongolia and China

Academic Vocabulary
eventual: taking place or becoming something at a later time; encounter: to meet

Sum It Up
The Mongols were fierce warriors who used terror to conquer. They learned about new weapons from the Chinese. They also held many of Asia's trade routes and taxed the products traded over the roads. They grew powerful and wealthy.

Mongol Rule in China

Evaluating
Mongol Rule: gave Mongol leaders top government jobs; let many Chinese keep their jobs; lived apart from Chinese society; tolerant of other religions; reached height of wealth and power; increased trade; enlarged the empire
Evaluation: Student evaluations will vary. Generally, students should weigh the positive results of Kublai Khan's leadership with actions they consider to be more negative. For example, do tolerance and increased trade outweigh living apart from Chinese society?

People to Meet
Kublai Khan: grandson of Genghis Khan; ruled as China's emperor; Marco Polo: traveler from Venice who went on fact-finding trips for Kublai Khan

Places to Locate
Karakorum: capital of Mongolia prior to Khanbaliq; Khanbaliq: Mongol's Chinese capital in northern China (present-day Beijing); Beijing: modern Chinese city that stands on the site of Khanbaliq

Sum It Up
Kublai Khan

Section Wrap-Up
- He was the leader who united the Mongols and built the Mongolian empire.
- Trade increased. China reached the height of its wealth and power and attracted foreign visitors. They built wide streets, beautiful palaces, and fine homes.

Read to Write Challenge
Students' descriptions should include religious tolerance, increased trade during the long peace, increased wealth, shipbuilding, and international relations.

Chapter 4, Section 4

Reading Strategy

Traded goods and spread culture
Merchants and China grew rich
Chinese officials did not like the cost or new ideas
The emperor ended the voyages after Zheng He's death

The Rise of the Ming

Monitoring Comprehension

Restored civil service exams
Carried out a census
Rebuilt farms and canals
Planted new forests and built new roads
Imported new types of rice
Supported the silk industry and encouraged farmers to start growing cotton and weaving cloth

Terms to Know

treason: an act against the government; a disloyal act; census: a count of the number of people; novel: a book with a long, made-up story

People to Meet

Zhu Yuanzhang: rebel leader who drove out the Mongols and founded the Ming dynasty; Yong Le: emperor of China; son of Hong Wu (Zhu Yuanzhang)

Places to Locate

Nanjing: capital in southern China of the Ming dynasty

Academic Vocabulary

erode: to wear down; compile: to put together, collect; drama: a story told by actors who pretend to be characters in the story

Terms to Review

Sample sentence:
Ming emperors made reforms to strengthen the government.

Sum It Up

the very center of the Imperial City where China's emperors lived

China Explores the World

Outlining

I. Who Was Zheng He?
   A. Emperor sent a fleet of ships on seven voyages meant to show off China's power and collect tribute.
   B. Zheng He was the leader of these voyages.
II. Where Did Zheng He Travel?
   A. Zheng He traveled to and traded with Asia, India, Arabia, and East Africa.
   B. China grew wealthy from the trade.
   C. Chinese officials did not like the voyages because merchants were growing rich and bringing in ideas from outside.
   D. After Zheng He's death, the emperor stopped the voyages.
III. The Europeans Arrive in China
   A. Portugal sent a fleet to China to trade and to share Christianity.
   B. The Chinese finally allowed them to set up a trading post at Macao.
   C. Christian missionaries came to China but did not convince many to convert.
IV. Why Did the Ming Dynasty Fall?
   A. Ming emperors held too much power, and the dynasty began to decline.
   B. The Manchus attacked, captured Beijing, and set up a new dynasty.

Terms to Know

barbarian: a person who is not civilized

Places to Locate

Portugal: European country that set up trading posts in China

People to Meet

Zheng He: Chinese Muslim and court official who went on voyages to other kingdoms to trade and collect tribute

Academic Vocabulary

contact: to meet or interact with others

Sum It Up

Ming emperors held too much power. Ming rulers became weak, and greedy officials took over the country. They taxed the peasants heavily, and they revolted. Law and order disappeared, leaving the country open to attack by the Manchus.

Section Wrap-Up

- They restored civil service exams, carried out a census to collect taxes, rebuilt farms and canals, planted new forests and built new roads, imported new types of rice, supported the silk industry, and encouraged farmers to start growing cotton.
- They made the government strong, made agriculture thrive, advanced Chinese culture, sent a fleet of ships to other lands, and expanded trade.

Read to Write Challenge

Students' essays should mention that China was at the height of its power during the Ming dynasty and did not need to change.

Chapter 5, Section 1

Reading Strategy

Animism; honor the kami at shrines; ask the kami for help; ritual cleansing to remove spiritual stains

Japan's Geography

Analyzing

Mountains: limited land to farm; forced people to turn to the sea to make a living; settled along the coast in fishing villages
Islands: encouraged people to become merchants; kept people isolated from the rest of Asia; Japan developed an independent society

Places to Locate

Japan: a chain of more than 3,000 islands in the northern Pacific Ocean;
Hokkaido: one of Japan's four largest islands;
Honshu: one of Japan's four largest islands;
Shikoku: one of Japan's four largest islands;
Kyushu: one of Japan's four largest islands

Academic Vocabulary

occur: to happen

Sum It Up

The ocean surrounding the islands isolated Japan from the rest of Asia. Japan developed its own independent society with unique religion, art, literature, and government.

The First Settlers

Interpreting

Yayoi: ancestors of the Japanese people today; culture emerged around 300 B.C.
Yamato: a clan that became rulers of Japan during the A.D. 500s; claimed to be descended from sun goddess
Jimmu: Yamato leader who claimed title of "emperor of heaven"; founded line of rulers in Japan
Akihito: current Japanese emperor; descended from Jimmu
Sequence: 1. Yayoi; 2. Yamato; 3. Jimmu; 4. Akihito

Terms to Know

clan: a group of families related by blood or marriage

Academic Vocabulary

portion: a part of a whole

People to Meet

Jimmu: Yamato chief that founded a line of Japanese rulers that has never been broken; took the title "emperor of heaven"

Sum It Up

During the A.D. 500s, a clan called the Yamato became strong enough to bring most of Japan under its rule.

Prince Shotoku's Reforms

Determining the Main Idea

Established government with powerful emperor who ruled with the help of trained officials; created a bureaucracy in which the emperor appointed all government officials; developed a constitution with rules for government based on ideas of Confucius; sent officials and students to China to study

Terms to Know

constitution: a written plan of government

People to Meet

Shotoku: prince who used Chinese government as a model for Japan's and created a constitution

Sum It Up

powerful emperor; Confucius's rules; art, medicine, philosophy; Buddhism; provincial government

What Is Shinto?

Summarizing

Sample answer: The religion of Shinto is based on nature spirits. Japanese worshiped the nature spirits and asked them for help.

Terms to Know

animism: the belief that all natural things have their own spirits; shrine: a holy place

Sum It Up

They worshiped at shrines. Priests, musicians, and dancers performed rituals for people who asked the gods for help.

Section Wrap-Up

- Japan's mountains meant people had limited land to farm. People turned to the sea to make a living and settled along the coast in fishing villages. Japan's islands encouraged people to become merchants. They also kept people isolated from the rest of Asia. Japan developed an independent society.
- Government: Japan built a strong central government modeled after China. Religion: Japanese beliefs developed into the religion of Shinto.

Read to Write Challenge

Students' interpretation of Shotoku's constitution will vary, but should be written in their own words. Students should describe the application of one of the rules.

Chapter 5, Section 2

Reading Strategy

Arrows point from Daimyo to land to Samurai to loyalty to Daimyo

Nara Japan

Inferring

1. The census counted all the people in the country and listed the lands where people lived and worked.
2. The people had to pay taxes in rice or silk cloth, and men had to serve in the army.
3. Student answers will vary. Generally, students should note that the emperor's power came from his control of the land and its crops. The census ensured that taxes and land were accounted for. It also ensured that the military stayed strong.

Academic Vocabulary

role: function, part to play

Terms to Review

Sample sentence:
The government census counted all the people in the land.

Sum It Up

Buddhists and non-Buddhists began to fight for power.

The Rise of the Shogun

Outlining

I. The Government Weakens
   A. In the A.D. 800s, regents became powerful as they ruled for weak emperors.
   B. Power moved from the emperor to the Fujiwara clan of regents who ruled the land.
   C. The government allowed the nobles to govern the lands under their control and collect taxes.

II. Who Were the Samurai?
   A. Nobles formed armies to protect their lands with warriors called samurai.
   B. Samurai fought on horseback with swords and bows and arrows.
   C. Samurai lived and fought by a strict code of conduct called Bushido.
   D. Samurai had a deep sense of loyalty and honor that carried over as far as World War II.

III. What Is a Shogun?
   A. The Minamoto family defeated the Taira family in a fight for control of the emperor and the government.
   B. The emperor gave Minamoto Yoritomo the title of shogun, or commander, to keep him loyal.
   C. The shogun set up his own government.
   D. The shoguns appointed high-ranking samurai to run the provinces, and they became the leading group in society.

IV. The Mongols Attack
   A. Violent Pacific storms stopped two attempts by Mongol emperor Kublai Khan to invade Japan.
   B. The Japanese named these winds kamikaze, or "divine wind."

Terms to Know

samurai: "to serve"; a Japanese warrior; shogun: Japanese commander of all the emperor's military forces

People to Meet

Minamoto Yoritomo: leader of the Minamoto family; first Japanese shogun

Places to Locate

Heian: capital city of Japan established by Emperor Kammu; Kamakura: headquarters of the shogunate military government set up by Yoritomo

Academic Vocabulary

conduct: behavior

Terms to Review

Sample sentence:
The regents from the Fujiwara clan were all part of the same family.

Sum It Up

He was the commander of the military government. Shoguns ran Japan's government for 700 years.

The Daimyo Divide Japan

Predicting

Student answers will vary. Students should apply knowledge from their reading of the previous sections as well as the opening paragraph to generate their prediction. Generally, they should have a sense that the government is weakening and that division and fighting will result.

Terms to Know

daimyo: powerful Japanese military lords who ruled their lands as independent kingdoms; vassal: person who serves another under an oath of loyalty; feudalism: the bond of loyalty between a lord and a vassal

People to Meet

Ashikaga Takauji: general who made himself shogun in 1333 and set up the Ashikaga shogunate

Sum It Up

Weak shoguns could not control the powerful daimyo, and fighting spread throughout the country.

Section Wrap-Up

- Buddhism came to Japan from Korea in the A.D. 500s. Government officials and nobles were the first to accept it. Then in the 600s and 700s, it spread rapidly among the common people.
- The shogun was the Japanese commander of all the emperor's military forces. The samurai was "one who serves," or a Japanese warrior.

Read to Write Challenge

Students' essays should describe how the Japanese system was not based on exams. It gave key government positions to nobles from powerful families. Those positions could be passed down from generation to generation.

Chapter 5, Section 3

Reading Strategy

Obey her father, husband, and son; marry to increase family wealth; work in the fields; cook; spin and weave cloth; care for children; help with family business

Japanese Religion and Culture

Analyzing

Pure Land: looked to Lord Amida, a Buddha of love and mercy; believers had to have faith in Amida and chant his name to get to his paradise in the clouds
Zen: find inner peace through self-control and a simple way of life; emphasized martial arts and meditation
Both: sects of Mahayana Buddhism

Terms to Know

sect: small religious group; martial arts: sports that involve fighting or self-defense; meditation: the practice of calming the mind to find inner peace; calligraphy: the art of fine handwriting; tanka: Japan's oldest form of poetry

Academic Vocabulary
involve: to be part of something; reveal: to make known or show plainly

People to Meet
Murasaki Shikibu: Japanese woman who wrote *The Tale of Genji,* believed to be the world's first novel

Terms to Review
Sample sentence:
I enjoy reading a long novel that tells a good story.

Sum It Up
Both teach self-control, leading to inner peace.

Economy and Society

Previewing
Student answers will vary. Answers may focus on the lives and roles of farmers, artisans, and women in the economy and society.

Terms to Know
guild: groups formed by artisans and merchants to protect and increase profits

Places to Locate
Kyoto: capital of Japan and center of production and trade

Academic Vocabulary
contribute: to give to a common purpose

Terms to Review
Sample sentence:
As people made, bought, and sold crafts and goods, Japan's economy grew.

Sum It Up
Nobles, military leaders, merchants, and artisans

Section Wrap-Up
- Sects of Buddhism (Pure Land and Zen) and Shinto impacted Japan's art, architecture, novels, and plays.
- Nobles, merchants, and artisans grew wealthy. Most Japanese were farmers who remained poor. Women remained restricted in many areas of life.

Read to Write Challenge
Students will create a poem in either tanka or haiku style. Tanka poems have five unrhymed lines and haiku poems have three lines with a total of 17 syllables.

Chapter 6, Section 1

Reading Strategy
King Clovis: king of the Franks; spread Catholicism
Charles Martel: mayor who defeated the Muslims at the Battle of Tours; Christianity remained Western Europe's major religion as a result of his victory
Charlemagne: Charles the Great; king who built an empire; crowned as Roman emperor by the pope
Otto I: German king who fought the Magyars and protected the pope; declared emperor of the Romans by the pope
Gregory the Great: Pope Gregory I who sent monks as missionaries into Europe

The Geography of Europe

Analyzing
Answers may include:
Peninsula: most of Europe within 300 miles of an ocean or sea; encouraged trade and fishing; helped economy grow
Seas and rivers: easy to travel in the interior of Europe; encouraged trade; provided safety; developed their own distinct ways of life and different cultures
Mountains: made it difficult for one group to rule all of Europe; encouraged independent kingdoms

Academic Vocabulary
significant: to have a lot of importance; instance: a case or example; enable: to make something possible

Sum It Up
Easy to travel in the interior of Europe; encouraged trade; provided safety; developed their own distinct ways of life and different cultures

The Germanic Kingdoms

Previewing
Student answers will vary. Students should generate questions based on the headings. Students should identify facts from their reading to answer the questions generated.

Terms to Know
fjord: steep-sided valleys that are inlets of the sea

People to Meet
Clovis: Frankish king who converted to Catholicism; Charles Martel: led Franks against Muslims; Charlemagne: king crowned by pope as new "Emperor of the Romans"

Sum It Up
The Vikings were people from Scandinavia who raided Europe. They were skilled sailors. They probably invaded Europe because Scandinavia's population had grown too big.

The Rise of the Catholic Church

Summarizing
Monks' roles included schooling people, providing food and rest to travelers, caring for the sick, and copying important written works.

Terms to Know
missionary: a person who is sent out to teach his or her religion; excommunicate: to exclude from church membership; concordat: an agreement between the pope and the ruler of a country

Academic Vocabulary
exclude: to keep out

People to Meet
Gregory VII: decreed that kings should not appoint church officials; Henry IV: Holy Roman emperor who refused to obey Gregory VII; was excommunicated

Sum It Up
They disagreed about the power of the pope versus the power of the king. Gregory excommunicated Henry over the disagreement. Henry asked forgiveness, but German nobles supporting Gregory still chose another king. Henry went to war, but Gregory's allies ultimately drove Henry's forces out.

Section Wrap-Up
- Geography, including the ocean and mountains, encouraged trade and the development of unique, independent kingdoms.
- Christianity became the dominant religion in Europe. The Catholic Church rose to the height of its power.

Read to Write Challenge
Students' predictions will vary, but should note that the height of power means it will lessen over time and kings would not appreciate being controlled.

Chapter 6, Section 2

Reading Strategy
Serf: could not be sold or have land taken away that was given to them; worked three days for the lord and the rest of the week growing food for themselves
Slave: could be sold; had no rights; worked all the time for the master
Both: served a lord or master; could not leave the manor, own property, or marry without the lord's approval

What Is Feudalism?

Visualizing
Answers will vary. Students should write from the perspective of a serf or a vassal. Their entries should reflect an understanding of their role in society as well as the duties and relationships. Students should use facts from their reading to support their writing.

Terms to Know
feudalism: system in which landowning nobles govern and protect people in return for services; vassal: a noble who obeyed a lord of higher rank; fief: the land granted to a vassal; knight: a warrior in armor who fought on horseback; serf: a peasant who performed services for a lord; they could not leave the manor, own property, or marry without the lord's approval

Academic Vocabulary
shift: change

Terms to Review

Sample sentence:
Japanese samurai, like knights, provided military service for their lords.

Sum It Up

A lord could be a vassal to a lord of a higher rank.

Life in Feudal Europe

Connecting

Student answers will vary. Generally, they should include a list of honorable behaviors and values that are important to them. Ask students to consider how these values are important to society as a whole.

Sum It Up

Rules of behavior that guided knights

Trade and Cities

Drawing Conclusions

Box 1: Trade resumes and increases
Box 2: Trade encourages manufacturing

Terms to Know

guild: organization of craftspeople; set prices and quality standards

Academic Vocabulary

process: method or plan

Sum It Up

Guilds set prices and standards for quality as well as decided who was allowed to join.

Section Wrap-Up

- Charlemagne's empire collapsed and Western Europe lost its strong central government. Landowning nobles became more and more powerful. The people turned to the nobles for protection.
- Life revolved around manors ruled by lords. Vassals or knights defended the lords. Serfs worked for the lords in return for protection. Nobles lived in castles. Peasants lived very humbly. Trade and city life grew.

Read to Write Challenge

Students' essays should describe how a money system changes how goods are exchanged. Merchants and traders became wealthy with money instead of goods as trade, manufacturing, and the economy grew. Guild members gained wealth and freedom, becoming a new middle class in Europe.

CHAPTER 6, SECTION 3

Reading Strategy

CAUSE	EFFECT
Muslims attack Byzantine Empire	Pope calls for a holy war
Crusaders capture Muslim region and establish Christian states	Muslims fight back and capture Edessa
Saladin captures Jerusalem	Third Crusade ends in a truce with Saladin

England in the Middle Ages

Monitoring Comprehension

1. King John raised taxes and punished his enemies without trials. The nobles resented his power.
2. The Great Council must agree to the king's taxes; freemen had the right to fair trials by their peers; the king and vassals had certain duties.
3. It helped establish the idea that people have rights and that the power of the government should be limited.

Terms to Know

grand jury: group that decides whether people should be accused of a crime; trial jury: group that decides whether an accused person is innocent or guilty

People to Meet

William the Conqueror: descendant of Viking ruler who became king of England; King John: king of England forced to sign the Magna Carta.

Academic Vocabulary

guarantee: to promise or pledge; document: a written statement

Sum It Up

The Magna Carta limited the king's power by guaranteeing the people certain rights.

The Kingdom of France

Evaluating

Philip IV: met with representatives from the clergy, nobles, and townspeople and peasants. This meeting became France's first parliament and first step toward representative government.
Evaluation: Student evaluations will differ. Students should use facts from their reading to support their evaluations. Generally, they should consider the fact that Philip had more power as king yet chose to share that power with his people.

Terms to Know

clergy: people ordained as priests

Sum It Up

He conquered the lands in western France held by England.

Eastern Europe and Russia

Drawing Conclusions

Student answers will vary. Possible answers include Oleg, Vladimir, Alexander Nevsky, and Ivan III. Students should use facts from their reading to support their conclusion.

Academic Vocabulary

nonetheless: in spite of some event

Terms to Review

Sample sentence:
Eastern Orthodox missionaries brought their faith to Russia.

Sum It Up

He led the Slavs of Novgorod in defeating the Swedes and Germans. For this, he was awarded the title of Grand Duke.

The Crusades

Sequencing

6 Emperor Frederick, King Richard I, and King Philip II join to fight Saladin.
2 The Crusaders create four states.
9 Muslims conquer all the territory lost in the First Crusade.
8 Crusaders burn and loot the Byzantine capital.
3 The Muslims capture Edessa.
1 The Crusaders capture Antioch and Jerusalem.
4 Saladin unites the Muslims and declares war against the Christian states.
7 King Richard I agrees to a truce with Saladin.
5 Saladin captures Jerusalem.

Sum It Up

In the First Crusade, the crusaders drove out the Muslims and set up four Christian states. In the Third Crusade, the crusaders reached a truce that meant Christians could travel to Jerusalem in safety.

Section Wrap-Up

- England and France established representative governments with parliaments. Russia was ruled by Grand Dukes and czars.
- Muslim Turks attacked the Byzantine Empire, and the emperor asked the pope for help to defend his Christian empire against Muslim invaders. The pope called on people to capture Jerusalem and free the Holy Land.

Read to Write Challenge

Students' essays should compare the Magna Carta to our own Bill of Rights, parliament to our own Congress, and common law and juries to their modern equivalent.

CHAPTER 6, SECTION 4

Reading Strategy

Romanesque: rectangular; rounded barrel vaults; windows set back in thick walls
Gothic: ribbed vaults and pointed arches; taller; flying buttresses; thinner walls with stained glass windows
Both: styles of cathedrals

Religion and Society

Questioning

Students' questions will vary. Questions should address main ideas in the text, including new religious orders, Francis of Assisi, popular religion, mass, the Inquisition, heresy, treatment of the Jews, and anti-Semitism.

Terms to Know

mass: the Catholic worship service; heresy: religious beliefs that go against church teachings; anti-Semitism: hatred of Jewish people

People to Meet
Francis of Assisi: founder of the first order of friars, the Franciscans

Academic Vocabulary
job: tasks, work

Sum It Up
Franciscans lived in towns and taught Christianity to the people. They helped poor people and spread their faith. Dominicans studied so they could defend church teachings and preach to well-educated people.

Medieval Culture

Determining the Main Idea
Sample answers:
1. Medieval art and architecture expressed the religious values of the culture through cathedrals.
2. The first European universities educated and trained scholars in the Middle Ages.
3. Thomas Aquinas was a Dominican friar who introduced new ideas, including scholasticism, natural law, and human rights.
4. Latin was the language of the church and literature in the Middle Ages, but people also spoke and wrote in the vernacular.

Terms to Know
theology: the study of religion and God; scholasticism: the use of reason to explore questions of faith; vernacular: everyday language used in a specific region

People to Meet
Thomas Aquinas: Dominican friar who spread the idea of scholasticism

Academic Vocabulary
demonstrate: show; obtain: to acquire or gain possession of

Terms to Review
Sample sentence:
Guilds trained and organized craftspeople.

Sum It Up
Natural law is the idea that some laws are part of human nature. These laws do not have to be made by governments.

Section Wrap-Up
- The Church was powerful in the Middle Ages. It played an important role in people's lives. Art and architecture centered on cathedrals. The Church used its power to try to prevent heresy and to get people to accept church teachings. It also persecuted the Jews.
- The first universities opened to promote learning. Thomas Aquinas spread the ideas of scholasticism, natural law, and human rights.

Read to Write Challenge
Students' essays should persuade Church leaders that heresy trials and persecution were wrong.

Chapter 6, Section 5

Reading Strategy
1330s: China
1340s: India and Makkah; Europe/Caffa and Sicily, France, Germany, England
1350s: Scandinavia, Eastern Europe, Russia

The Black Death

Inferring
Students should base their answer on the effects of the plague. With fewer people, trade declined and wages rose. Landlords had to pay more to get workers and charge less rent to get tenants. This gave peasants the power to bargain. This changed the social order.

Terms to Know
plague: a disease that spreads quickly and kills many people

Academic Vocabulary
approximate: an estimate of

Sum It Up
As many as 19–38 million, or nearly one out of every two people.

A Troubled Continent

Reviewing

Groups in Conflict	Name of Conflict	The Cause	The Effects
France and England	The 100 Years' War	English king Edward III declared himself king of France	France developed a strong government; England was weakened
Nobles in England fighting a civil war	Wars of the Roses	Nobles fought over who should be king	The winner, Henry Tudor, became King Henry VII
Spain and Portugal, and the Muslims	*Reconquista*	Christians opposed Muslim rule and fought to take back the Iberian Peninsula	Muslims lose all land but Granada; Ferdinand and Isabella conquer Granada and expel the Muslims; Spanish Inquisition

Terms to Know
Reconquista: Spain and Portugal's fight to take back the Iberian Peninsula from the Muslims

People to Meet
Joan of Arc: girl who led the French army; she was burned at the stake by the English; Isabella of Castile: queen of Spain; set up the Spanish Inquisition; Ferdinand of Aragon: king of Spain; set up the Spanish Inquisition

Places to Locate
Crécy: location in France of the first major battle of the Hundred Years' War; Orléans: city where Joan of Arc's faith stirred the French army; the French took the city

Academic Vocabulary
abandon: to leave without notice

Sum It Up
English king Edward III declared himself king of France

Section Wrap-Up
- A plague that wiped out nearly half the population in Europe and helped end the feudal system
- The Hundred Years' War, the Wars of the Roses, and the *Reconquista*

Read to Write Challenge
Students' narratives may include Charles's requests for Joan to meet with priests to determine whether to trust her faith.

Chapter 7, Section 1

Reading Strategy
Trade, banking, shipbuilding

The Italian Renaissance

Analyzing
Effect/Cause: City-states compete to produce works; bigger cities mean more customers and more money for art; bigger cities mean more discussion about art
Effect: The Renaissance begins

Terms to Know
Renaissance: "rebirth"; period in European history from about 1350 to 1550 when there was a rebirth of interest in art and learning; secular: more interested in this world than in religion

Places to Locate
Florence: important Italian city-state of the Renaissance; Venice: important Italian city-state of the Renaissance

Sum It Up
Italy had been the center of the Roman empire; cities had money to afford to pay artists; city-states competed to increase their fame

The Rise of Italy's City-States

Previewing
Student questions should be based on the headings and terms in the reading. Questions should relate to the growth of wealth in Italian city-states, Marco Polo, the wealth of Florence, the Medicis, and the rise of Venice.

People to Meet
Marco Polo: merchant from Venice who traveled all over China for Kublai Khan; his stories helped increase interest in China; Medici: Florence's richest family; bankers

Academic Vocabulary
network: a system of interconnected hubs
publish: to prepare printed material for public distribution

Terms to Review

Sample sentence:

The caravans carrying goods from China to the Middle East were protected by the Mongols.

Sum It Up

through trade and banking

The Urban Noble

Responding

Student responses will vary. They should show an understanding of Machiavelli's ideas. Students should be specific in their responses, supporting their opinions with facts.

Terms to Know

doge: a duke; diplomacy: the art of making deals with other countries

People to Meet

Niccolò Machiavelli: diplomat in Florence who wrote *The Prince*

Sum It Up

Medieval nobles got their wealth from land and looked down on merchants. Renaissance nobles mixed with merchants to form a new upper class.

Section Wrap-Up

- People in Italy remembered the Roman empire, cities grew wealthy and had money to pay artists, and city-states competed in art to increase their fame.
- City-states grew wealthy through trade, banking, and ship building.
- They made their living through trade, banking, and public life.

Read to Write Challenge

Students can use any of several options to illustrate or explain the information they find. They should use maps and other documents to help show where the Renaissance ideas began and how it spread to many different nations.

Chapter 7, Section 2

Reading Strategy

Alighieri: wrote *The Divine Comedy*

Chaucer: wrote *The Canterbury Tales* in vernacular English

Gutenberg: invented the printing press

Shakespeare: wrote dozens of plays such as *Hamlet, Macbeth,* and *Romeo and Juliet*

Cervantes: wrote *Don Quixote de la Mancha*

Renaissance Humanism

Summarizing

Sample answers:

1. Italians studied ancient Roman and Greek literature, art, and architecture to understand it.
2. Humanism set balance between religion and human needs. It urged people to work to better their cities.

Terms to Know

humanism: belief that the individual and human society are important; values a balance between faith and reason

People to Meet

Leonardo da Vinci: great Renaissance painter, scientist, inventor, and engineer

Terms to Review

Sample sentence:

Scientists study anatomy to learn about the workings of the human body.

Sum It Up

They viewed the writings with great respect and studied them to increase their knowledge of many subjects.

Changes in Literature

Scanning

1. It is a story about 29 pilgrims on a journey to the city of Canterbury.
2. Cervantes was from Spain.

Terms to Know

vernacular: everyday language of people in a particular region

Places to Locate

Canterbury: English city that was the focus of *The Canterbury Tales*

People to Meet

Dante Alighieri: poet from Florence, Italy, who wrote *The Divine Comedy;* Johannes Gutenberg: invented the printing press; William Shakespeare: greatest writer in Elizabethan era

Academic Vocabulary

debate: a contention by words or arguments; credit: recognition

Sum It Up

More people could read literature, so ideas could spread more easily.

Section Wrap-up

- Humanism is the belief that the individual and human society are important. It seeks to balance faith and reason. Humanism led to study and an increase in learning.
- Literature became more popular because it was written in the vernacular of the people. The printing press also made it much cheaper and easier to print books, so they were more readily available.

Read to Write Challenge

Students should be encouraged to be creative and use their imaginations.

Chapter 7, Section 3

Reading Strategy

Renaissance art: showed people in real life, showed emotions, use of perspective, realistic look using *chiaroscuro*

Artists in Renaissance Italy

Inferring

Differences: tried to show real life; tried to show emotion; used perspective to make art more realistic; used *chiaroscuro* to add drama and emotion

Effect of humanism: Humanism emphasized the importance of the individual. It balanced faith and reason. In the same way, Renaissance art emphasized the individual. It didn't just convey a religious message. It portrayed religious messages with a focus on the emotions and the uniqueness of the individuals involved.

Terms to Know

chiaroscuro: use of light and shadows to soften edges; fresco: painting technique in which watercolor paints are applied over wet plaster

People to Meet

Sandro Botticelli: painter from Florence who painted frescoes in the Sistine Chapel; Raphael Sanzio: painter who painted the *School of Athens;* Michelangelo Buonarroti: painter and sculptor; painted the ceiling of the Sistine Chapel; Titian: painter from Venice who used rich colors and extremely dark shadows

Academic Vocabulary

differentiate: to become distinct or different in character; perspective: representation in a drawing or painting of parallel lines as converging in order to give the illusion of depth and distance

Sum It Up

Medieval art focused on conveying a religious message. Instead, Renaissance art portrayed messages with a focus on the emotions and the uniqueness of the individuals involved.

The Renaissance Spreads

Connecting

Student paragraphs will vary. Students should describe the work of art, their reaction to it, and specific techniques used by the artist that made the art more real to them.

Places to Locate

Flanders: an area located in present-day northern Belgium

People to Meet

Jan Van Eyck: master of oil painting known for his brilliant colors; Albrecht Dürer: one of the greatest Northern Renaissance artists from Germany, best known for his engravings

Terms to Review

Sample sentence:

Quixote pretends he is a knight, so he lives by the code of chivalry.

Sum It Up

The Northern Renaissance took place in present-day Belgium, Luxembourg, Germany, and the Netherlands. Northern artists used different methods to achieve realism. They developed oil painting.

Section Wrap-Up

- Renaissance art tried to portray real life and emotions using new methods, including perspective and *chiaroscuro*.
- Northern Renaissance artists developed oil painting.

Read to Write Challenge

Student essays should examine elements of Renaissance art, such as *chiaroscuro*, perspective, fresco. They can also examine movements in sculpting, music, or writing.

Chapter 8, Section 1

Reading Strategy

Bishops behaved like kings; the Church taxed peasants heavily; priests could barely read or give a good sermon; questions about the pope's power; the sale of indulgences; the means of salvation (a gift from God versus good works)

Calls for Church Reform

Outlining

I. What Ideas Led to the Reformation?
   A. Desiderius Erasmus was a Christian humanist who said humans could use their reason to become better Christians.
   B. Erasmus wanted to translate the Bible into the vernacular so all people could read it.

II. The Church Upsets Reformers
   A. By the 1300s, many people were upset with the Church's focus on money.
   B. In the 1500s, the pope sold indulgences to repair the church of St. Peter's in Rome.
   C. The sale of indulgences outraged Martin Luther. He was also angry at Church leaders who allowed people to think an indulgence could pardon sin.
   D. John Wycliffe also questioned the pope's power and wanted everyone to read the Bible.

III. Who Was Martin Luther?
   A. Martin Luther was angered by the behavior of Church leaders and worried about his own soul.
   B. Luther prayed, fasted, and searched the Bible to learn about salvation.
   C. The Church told Luther he would be saved through faith and good works and receiving the sacraments.
   D. By studying the Bible, Luther concluded that he was saved by faith, and not by good works.
   E. Luther listed his arguments against indulgences, and copies were read all across the German kingdoms.

IV. Revolt Leads to New Churches
   A. The pope and Luther argued, and the pope excommunicated Luther.
   B. Luther's ideas led to a new denomination known as Lutheranism.
   C. Lutheranism states that salvation comes through faith, the Bible is the final source of truth, and the church is made up of all its believers.

V. Peasant Revolts
   A. Peasants who lived very hard lives were stirred to revolt by Luther's ideas.
   B. The nobles defeated the peasants.
   C. Luther criticized the nobles for their treatment of the peasants.
   D. Luther told the peasants that they must obey the government established by God.

Terms to Know

Reformation: movement started by Martin Luther that challenged the Catholic Church and led to new Christian churches; indulgence: a reduction in the Church's punishment for a sin; denomination: an organized branch of Christianity

People to Meet

Martin Luther: man who initiated the break from the Catholic Church that led to a revolution in Christianity; Desiderius Erasmus: chief leader of Christian humanism religious movement; John Wycliffe: English priest who preached that Jesus Christ, not the pope had power over people; William Tyndale: translated the Bible into English and printed the New Testament in 1525.

Places to Locate

Wittenburg: town in Germany where Martin Luther taught in a university

Academic Vocabulary:

conclude: to decide on something by reasoning

Terms to Review

Sample sentences:
The Roman clergy, or leaders of the church, were not happy with Luther's ideas.
The pope excommunicated Luther, so Luther was no longer a member of the Church.

Sum It Up

Luther became angry and posted the reasons he opposed indulgences. This led to the Reformation.

Politics and Lutheranism

Synthesizing

Student paragraphs will vary. Students should incorporate ideas from current events, history, and their reading to support their views. They should consider what happens when power and politics mix with religion. They should evaluate the decision of many German rulers to leave the Church for political reasons.

Academic Vocabulary

energy: vigorous exertion of power; resource: a source of supply or support; convert: to change from one belief, view, or party to another

Sum It Up

Many realized they could increase their own power by leaving the Church. They could rule their own kingdoms, earn income from monasteries, and collect tax for themselves.

Section Wrap Up

- Luther's ideas led to the Reformation and to many new churches and denominations.
- Political leaders supported Protestantism because they wanted more power. Protestant rulers could seize lands owned by the Catholic Church. The Catholic Church and the pope could no longer tax the people, so rulers could keep money for themselves.

Read to Write Challenge

Students' essays should explore some of Luther's biographical information, as well as his primary arguments for challenging the Roman Catholic Church. Luther's ideas caused many to break from the Catholic Church, and to question their governments. Even within the Catholic Church, Luther's challenge provoked a serious reform movement.

Chapter 8, Section 2

Reading Strategy

Henry VIII: forms the Church of England after the pope refuses to annul his marriage to Catherine
Mary I: Queen of England who tried to restore Catholic Church to power; she arrested and executed many Protestants
Elizabeth I: Queen of England after Mary I who restored the Anglican Church

Calvin and Calvinism

Scanning

1. born in France in the early 1500s; studied theology; heard ideas of Luther; went to Geneva; was a powerful preacher who convinced many to follow him
2. shares many ideas with Luther; main idea is predestination; encouraged people to work hard and behave; believed that congregations should choose their own elders and ministers to run the church

Terms to Know

theology: the study of questions about God; predestination: the idea that God has already decided who will go to heaven and who will not

People to Meet

John Calvin: founder of Calvinism, which preached predestination

Places to Locate
Geneva: Protestant city in Switzerland where John Calvin found safety

Academic Vocabulary
clarify: to make understandable; consent: to give assent or approval

Sum it Up
Calvin believed in predestination, the idea that God had already decided who would go to heaven. He also believed that congregations should choose their own ministers.

The English Reformation

Predicting
Student predictions will vary. Predictions should be based on their prior reading. Generally, they should anticipate fighting between Catholics and Protestants.

Terms to Know
annul: to cancel a marriage

Places to Locate
London: main city in England where monarchs lived; location of the Tower of London

People to Meet
Henry VIII: English king who created the Anglican Church; Mary I: English queen and daughter of Henry who wanted to make England Catholic; known as "Bloody Mary"; Elizabeth I: English queen and half-sister of Mary who restored the Anglican Church; one of the greatest rulers in English history

Terms to Review
Sample sentence:
The pope excommunicated Henry, or expelled him from the church.

Sum It Up
He wanted to annul his marriage so he could remarry and get a male heir to the throne. When the pope refused, Henry turned to the archbishop of Canterbury. In response, the pope excommunicated Henry, and Henry declared that the king was the head of the Church in England.

Section Wrap-Up
- Calvin believed in predestination, the idea that God had already decided who would go to heaven. He also believed that congregations should choose their own ministers.
- Henry VIII wanted an annulment of his marriage with his wife Catherine. The pope refused to grant it, so Henry formed his own church.

Read to Write Challenge
Essays should point out Calvin's belief in predestination and that congregations should choose their own ministers. Luther rejected the Catholic idea of indulgences, and believed that God's graciousness, rather than human works, led to salvation.

Chapter 8, Section 3

Reading Strategy
Council of Trent made Catholic beliefs clear and set up rules for bishops and priests
Set up seminaries to train priests
Recognized the Jesuit order of priests to fight heresy

Counter-Reformation

Monitoring Comprehension
France: The Huguenots fought the Catholics in a 30-year civil war; Henry of Navarre becomes a Catholic so he can rule France; he gives the Huguenots the right to worship freely
Bohemia: The worst religious war of the Reformation era; Protestant churches in Bohemia rebelled against the Catholic king; it became a war of kingdoms; towns were wiped out; Spain was weakened; France became one of Europe's most powerful countries
Spain: Ferdinand and Isabella decide that all subjects should be Catholic to keep the country strong; they expel Muslims and Jews; they set up the Spanish Inquisition

Terms to Know
seminary: special school for training and educating priests; heresy: a religious belief that contradicts Church teaching

People to Meet
Ignatius of Loyola: man from Spain who founded the Jesuits, a new order of priests; Huguenot: French Protestants; King Ferdinand: King of Spain; Queen Isabella: Queen of Spain; Maimonides: Jewish scholar from Spain

Places to Locate
Trent: city near Rome where the pope called a council to make Catholic beliefs clear; Navarre: kingdom in southern France ruled by Huguenot nobles; home of King Henry IV; Paris: main city in France

Academic Vocabulary
contradict: to express a different point of view; impact: to strike forcefully; philosophy: pursuit of wisdom; eliminate: to cast out or get rid of

Terms to Review
Sample sentences:
The pope led reforms in the Catholic Church by setting up a church council at Trent.
The Catholic clergy were told to work hard to keep people's faith.

Sum It Up
He became a Catholic.

Legacy of the Reformation

Drawing Conclusions
Student responses will vary.
1. Political and economic power of the Catholic Church decreased greatly
2. Kings claimed divine right to rule
3. Catholics began sending missionaries around the world

In Europe, the Catholic Church lost a lot of power. Although it maintained a lot of influence, the church had to send missionaries around the world to try to convert new lands to Catholicism.

Terms to Know
divine right: authority granted to a king directly from God

People to Meet
Francis Xavier: first Jesuit missionary to Japan

Sum It Up
the Americas, Asia (Japan, the Philippine Islands and Vietnam)

Section Wrap-Up
- The Catholic Church responded to the Reformation with the Counter-Reformation. This was a series of changes designed to address problems in the Church. These changes included setting strict rules for the clergy, new seminaries to train priests, and the Jesuit order of priests.
- As the Catholic Church weakened, kings asserted their divine right to power.

Read to Write Challenge
Student essays should point out that torture and execution were widely used. Anyone found in disfavor with the church could be accused of heresy. Thousands were executed.

Chapter 9, Section 1

Reading Strategy

Olmec	Near present-day Vera Cruz, Mexico	1200 B.C. to 400 B.C.	Farmed, used rivers for trade, made mirrors and carved stone heads
Moche	Peru	A.D. 100 to A.D. 700	Used irrigation, farmed, hunted, fished, built huge pyramids, traded pottery, jewelry, and cloth

Farming Begins in Mesoamerica

Analyzing
Glaciers melted and the land bridge to America disappeared
Some animals became extinct
Warm weather opened new opportunities to early Americans to learn to farm

Terms To Know
glacier: a huge sheet of ice

Places to Locate
Beringia: land bridge between Asia and Alaska; Mesoamerica: region in North America between Mexico and Costa Rica (present-day Central America)

3. Catholics began sending missionaries around the world

In Europe, the Catholic Church lost a lot of power. Although it maintained a lot of influence, the church had to send missionaries around the world to try to convert new lands to Catholicism.

Terms to Know

divine right: authority granted to a king directly from God

People to Meet

Francis Xavier: first Jesuit missionary to Japan

Sum It Up

the Americas, Asia (Japan, the Philippine Islands and Vietnam)

Section Wrap-Up

- The Catholic Church responded to the Reformation with the Counter-Reformation. This was a series of changes designed to address problems in the Church. These changes included setting strict rules for the clergy, new seminaries to train priests, and the Jesuit order of priests.
- As the Catholic Church weakened, kings asserted their divine right to power.

Read to Write Challenge

Student essays should point out that torture and execution were widely used. Anyone found in disfavor with the church could be accused of heresy. Thousands were executed.

Chapter 9, Section 1

Reading Strategy

Olmec	Near present-day Vera Cruz, Mexico	1200 B.C. to 400 B.C.	Farmed, used rivers for trade, made mirrors and carved stone heads
Moche	Peru	A.D. 100 to A.D. 700	Used irrigation, farmed, hunted, fished, built huge pyramids, traded pottery, jewelry, and cloth

Farming Begins in Mesoamerica

Analyzing

Glaciers melted and the land bridge to America disappeared
Some animals became extinct
Warm weather opened new opportunities to early Americans to learn to farm

Terms To Know

glacier: a huge sheet of ice

Places to Locate

Beringia: land bridge between Asia and Alaska; Mesoamerica: region in North America between Mexico and Costa Rica (present-day Central America)

Academic Vocabulary:

environment: the complex of physical, chemical, and biotic factors that act upon an organism or an ecological community

Sum it Up

When the Ice Age ended and the climate warmed, people discovered that they could plant seeds, which would grow into crops they could eat.

Early American Civilizations

Drawing Conclusions

Olmec: built big trading empire; Maya: traded throughout Mesoamerica; reached as far as southern Mexico and Central America; Toltec: built the city of Tula; conquered lands; controlled trade; Moche: irrigated the land; traded as far away as the Amazon River valley; Inca: built the largest empire in the ancient Americas.

Student conclusions will vary. Generally, they should note that the civilizations developed trade and technology and systems to rule large empires. They should speculate about the advanced level of these societies.

Terms To Know

monopoly: sole right

People To Meet

Olmec: one of the earliest Mesoamerican civilizations; built a large trading empire near present-day Vera Cruz, Mexico; Maya: early Mesoamerican civilization located on the Yucatan Peninsula; Toltec: early Mesoamerican civilization; built the city of Tula near present-day Mexico City; Moche: early Mesoamerican civilization located in present-day Peru; built huge pyramids; Inca: built largest empire in the ancient Americas

Places To Locate

Teotihuacán: "Place of the Gods"; the first planned city in the Americas, built by the Olmec; Yucatán Peninsula: peninsula located in Mexico where the Mayan civilization was centered; Cuzco: capital of the Incan empire

Academic Vocabulary

design: to create, fashion, execute, or construct according to plan

Sum It Up

No one is sure. Historians suspect overpopulation, a drought, or rebellion.

Section Wrap-Up

- People from Asia came to the Americas over a land bridge that disappeared under the sea at the end of the Ice Age.
- They were farmers, traders, and hunters. They used technology including irrigation. They built huge trading empires with large cities.

Read to Write Challenge

Students should show their research abilities, as well as their ability to map information.

Chapter 9, Section 2

Reading Strategy

Top: Rulers and their wives
Head priest and army commander
Regional army leaders
Temple priests, army commanders, and skilled workers
Farmers, herders, and ordinary soldiers

The Mayan People

Scanning

Possible answers include
Discovery of Mayan civilization: in 1839 by John Lloyd Stevens and Frederick Catherwood
Government: organized in city-states; rulers supplied leadership and military force; leadership passed from king to king

Terms to Know

sinkhole: area where the earth has collapsed

Academic Vocabulary

source: a point of origin; cooperate: to act or work with another or others

Places to Locate

Petén: a flat, densely forested area in present-day Guatemala, home to the Mayan civilization

Sum It Up

A ready water supply

Mayan Culture

Questioning

Student responses will vary.

1. Q: What did Mayan people build to honor their rulers? A: pyramids
2. Q: Who was Chac? A: the God of rain and sunlight
3. Q: What did Mayan hieroglyphics represent? A: symbols represented sounds, words, or ideas.

Terms to Know

alliance: political agreement between people or states to work together

People to Meet

Jasaw Chan K'awiil I: a ruler of the Mayan people

Sum It Up

They were used for heavy labor or household chores by the elite ruling class.

The Aztec

Drawing Conclusions

1. They expected their kings to prove themselves by leading troops into battle.
2. Soldiers who died in battle, captives who gave their lives in sacrifice, and women who died in childbirth. The Aztec saw death as honorable.
3. Heavy use of irrigation, fertilization, and draining of swamps

Responses will vary. Generally students should conclude that battle and conquest were a large part of Aztec life. Additionally, death played a significant role in their society, through sacrifice and battle.

Terms to Know

codices: small Aztec books that recorded history and religion

Places to Locate

Tenochtitlán : great Aztec city built in a marsh

Sum It Up

By performing one act of bravery during war

Life in the Inca Empire

Determining the Main Idea

Main Idea: Pachacuti was a strong king who united the Inca Empire.
Supporting Ideas: Set up a strong central government, but let local rulers stay in power; required people to learn a common language; designed a system of roads

Terms To Know

quipu: rope knotted with cords of different lengths and colors, used to do mathematical calculations

People to Meet

Pachacuti: name of a great Incan ruler

Places to Locate

Machu Picchu: a retreat built for Incan kings

Sum It Up

He took their sons to Cuzco for training.

Section Wrap-Up

- The Mayan, Incan, and Aztec cultures developed in present-day Central and South America. They were warrior peoples who developed organized governments, religious systems, and social hierarchies. They also developed ideas in science and math and built tremendous cities and monuments.
- The environment in different parts of North America affected the way people lived, including their ability to farm, hunt or fish; their homes; and their diet.

Read to Write Challenge

Descriptive essays should demonstrate students' ability to research and explain the processes most likely used by these ancient people. Some description of a particular example, with interesting facts about the building, will be helpful.

Chapter 9, Section 3

Reading Strategy

Used horses and guns to shock Native Americans; used Malintzin as an interpreter; formed alliances; was aided by disease; the fall of the Aztec and Inca empires

Spain Conquers Mexico

Visualizing

Student answers will vary. Paragraphs should reflect facts from the reading, including the frightening appearance of the soldiers, the dogs, and the guns, as well as the enslavement of the Taino.

Terms to Know

conquistador: a Spanish soldier-explorer sent to the Americas

People to Meet

Christopher Columbus: discovered Haiti and the Dominican Republic trying to find westward sea route to Asia; Hernán Cortés: a Spanish conquistador; Montezuma II: Aztec emperor defeated by Cortés; Malintzin: a Mayan woman who helped Cortés defeat the Aztecs

Places to Locate

Hispaniola: island in the Caribbean discovered by Columbus; Extremadura: part of Spain with poor soil and hot summers

Academic Vocabulary

finance: to pay for or financially support; generate: to bring into existence

Sum It Up

Spanish soldier-explorers sent to the Americas

Pizarro Conquers the Inca

Analyzing

Possible answers include: Pizarro knew how to fight; he had learned from Cortés; he knew a lot about Native Americans; the Incas misjudged Pizarro and failed to act; the emperor did not bring protection to this meeting with Pizarro

Terms To Know

treason: disloyalty to the government

People to Meet

Francisco Pizarro: defeated the Inca

Sum It Up

He did not free him when Atahualpa gave him gold and silver. He charged the emperor with crimes that led to death.

Section Wrap-Up

- Cortés used horses and guns to shock Native Americans; he used Malintzin as an interpreter; he formed alliances; he was aided by disease in his defeat of the Aztecs. Pizarro conquered the Inca.
- Pizarro tricked the Incan emperor to defeat him. The emperor underestimated Pizarro and did not bring enough protection to their meeting. Pizarro captured the emperor and took over the empire.

Read to Write Challenge

The narrative essay should provide biographical information about the conquistador, including background, how he came to the Americas, and his accomplishments while there.

Chapter 10, Section 1

Reading Strategy

Merchants wanted new trade routes to Asia; new technology helped navigation; stronger nations could fund exploration

Europe Gets Ready to Explore

Summarizing

Sample answers:

1. Europeans wanted to trade directly with Asia by sea to avoid paying higher prices for trade in the Middle East.
2. New and rediscovered technologies, including the astrolabe, compass, and rudder, made it possible for ships to travel the Atlantic Ocean.
3. The growth of towns and trade made four European governments powerful and wealthy enough to explore.
4. Europeans studied ancient maps and Arab books to learn the geography of East Africa and the Indian Ocean.

Terms to Know

astrolabe: ancient Greek device used to find latitude; compass: invented by the Chinese, helps locate magnetic north; caravel: a Portuguese ship; cartography: science of mapmaking

Academic Vocabulary:

fund: to provide money or other resources

Sum It Up

The desire to trade directly with Asia; new technology for sailing and shipbuilding; the rise of strong nations wealthy enough to pay for exploration; and knowledge gained from ancient maps and Arab books

Exploring the World

Questioning

Student questions should be based on the headings and terms in the reading. Questions should relate to Henry the Navigator, Vasco da Gama, Christopher Columbus, Ferdinand Magellan, the Strait of Magellan, English and French explorers, John Cabot, Jacques Cartier, or Spain's fight with England.

Places to Locate

Azores: islands captured by the Portuguese; Madeira: island captured by the Portuguese; Hispaniola: island explored by Columbus; Strait of Magellan: passage around South America explored by Magellan; Newfoundland: large island named by John Cabot; St. Lawrence River: river in North America explored by Jacques Cartier

People to Meet
Vasco da Gama: Portuguese explorer, the first to round the tip of Africa and cross the Indian Ocean; Christopher Columbus: Italian navigator who landed in the Americas and claimed them for Spain; Ferdinand Magellan: Spanish explorer who discovered a passage around South America to the Pacific Ocean; John Cabot: English explorer who searched for a northern route to Asia; Jacques Cartier: French explorer who sailed into the St. Lawrence River seeking a passage to Asia

Academic Vocabulary
locate: to determine or indicate the place, or site

Sum It Up
Vasco da Gama; Magellan's crew

Section Wrap-up
- rise of strong kingdoms, trade, technology
- Spain, England, France, Portugal; India, Cuba, Hispaniola, the Americas

Read to Write Challenge
Students' expository essays should identify the working components of the device they selected, as well as a thorough explanation of how a sailor used the device to determine the ship's position.

Chapter 10, Section 2

Reading Strategy
mercantilism, investments, cottage industry

Europe's Empires

Determining the Main Idea
The Spanish and Portuguese built new empires by establishing colonies in the Americas.

Places to Locate
Netherlands: area of northern Europe where Protestantism took hold

People to Meet
Henry VIII: founded Anglican Church after breaking from Catholicism; Elizabeth I: queen of England

Academic Vocabulary
primary: first in order of importance or development; aid: to give assistance

Sum It Up
The Spanish conquered both the Incas and the Aztecs, two large civilizations.

The Commercial Revolution

Analyzing
Mercantilism
Colonies
Commerce
Joint-stock companies
Cottage industry

Terms to Know
mercantilism: the idea that a country gets more power by building up its supply of gold and silver; export: to sell goods to other countries; import: to buy goods from other countries; colony: a group of people living in a new area controlled by their home country; commerce: the buying and selling of goods in large amounts over long distances; invest: to put money into a project; capitalism: economic system in which people, not government, own property and make goods

Places to Locate
Moluccas: the Spice Islands of Southeast Asia; served as a Portuguese trading post

People to Meet
Pedro Alvares Cabral: Portuguese leader who fought against Muslim merchants in the Indian Ocean

Academic Vocabulary
anticipate: to look forward to

Sum It Up
Entrepreneurs invested money in the project. For larger projects, a group of entrepreneurs came together to form a joint-stock company. Merchants also asked peasants to make goods for them so they could buy goods at lower prices.

Section Wrap-Up
- They established colonies in the Americas.
- Europeans set up colonies and created joint-stock companies to increase trade.

Read to Write Challenge
Comparative essays should describe advantages such as profits, investments, shared risk for ventures, competition. Disadvantages should include potential for monopolies or uncontrolled pricing, risk of investing, risk of only a few individuals controlling most of the wealth.

Chapter 10, Section 3

Reading Strategy
Positive Effects: World's food supply increased; corn and potatoes were taken to North America; Europeans spread religion, political ideas, and expanded economies
Negative Effects: European diseases spread; European plants and animals hurt local environments; eliminated native cultures

The Columbian Exchange

Skimming
Corn fed to European animals resulted in healthier animals with more meat, leather, and wool. More potatoes could be grown than grain, feeding more people from the same amount of land. Italians used tomatoes for sauce. Europeans created chocolate candy and began smoking tobacco.

Terms to Know
Columbian Exchange: exchange of people, goods, technology and ideas between Europe and the Americas; pampas: grassy plains

Places to Locate
Argentina: country in South America; Great Plains: vast plains area in North America

Academic Vocabulary
transfer: to convey from one person, place, or situation to another

Sum it Up
It is the global exchange of people, goods, technology, ideas, and diseases.

Problems with the Exchange

Previewing
Student responses will vary.
This passage looks at the problems that occurred with global exchange. These problems included disease, damage to environments, destruction of cultures, and slavery.

Terms to Know
East India Company: built a British trade empire in India; Dutch East India Company: built a trade empire in Indonesia

Places to Locate
Caribbean: region of islands in the gulf between North and South America

Academic Vocabulary
positive: constructive or desirable

Terms to Review
Sample sentences:
The Japanese shogun, or military ruler, defeated the feudal lords.
The new shogun defeated the feudal lords, the daimyo.

Sum It Up
Spread of germs and disease wiped out millions of people; some species of plant and animals damaged local environments; slavery became widespread in the Caribbean and in the Americas

Section Wrap-Up
- The exchange of goods and ideas across the world.
- New food sources help feed more people; employment for workers; horses for Native American hunting; Japan is reunited; slavery; Europeans take over parts of Asia and India; germs and disease

Read to Write Challenge
Expository essays should explain the origins of the company as a monopoly trade organization between England and India. Eventually, this organization grew so powerful that it ruled India for a time.

Boyle: all substances are made up of elements that cannot be broken down
Lavoisier: materials need oxygen to burn

People to Meet

Newton: proposed the universal law of gravitation

Sum It Up

Gravity

The Triumph of Reason

Sequencing

Observe facts
Make a hypothesis
Predict a result
Test the prediction with experiment and observation
Modify the hypothesis

Terms to Know

rationalism: the belief that reason is the chief source of knowledge; scientific method: the process used in scientific research to collect and analyze evidence; hypothesis: an explanation of facts

People to Meet

Descartes: French scientific thinker, viewed as the founder of rationalism; said "I think, therefore I am"

Sum It Up

It is the process used in scientific research to collect and analyze evidence. It outlines five steps: Observe facts, make a hypothesis, predict a result, test the prediction with experiment and observation, modify the hypothesis

Section Wrap-Up

- Scientific knowledge grew. Christian thinkers tried to show that Christianity and reason could go together. New universities opened. Technology and voyages of exploration resulted in growing knowledge of different parts of the world. All of this set the stage for a new understanding of the natural world that would change the way people viewed the universe.
- It is the process used in scientific research to collect and analyze evidence. It outlines five steps: Observe facts, make a hypothesis, predict a result, test the prediction with experiment and observation, modify the hypothesis. New scientific learning and the scientific method led people to look more to reason as the source of knowledge.

Read to Write Challenge

Persuasive essays should demonstrate the student's ability to write persuasively and to use facts to help support the argument.

Chapter 11, Section 2

Reading Strategy

Thomas Hobbes: natural law made absolute monarchy the best form of government
John Locke: natural law affirmed citizens' rights and made government answerable to the people
Montesquieu: admired England's government and supported the separation of powers
Voltaire: people should be free to choose their own religion; deism
Diderot: attacked superstition and supported freedom of religion
Mary Wollstonecraft: supported women's rights
Rousseau: people should live simpler lives closer to nature; social contract

New Ideas About Politics

Analyzing

Hobbes: absolute monarchy is the best form of government; humans can't be trusted to make their own decisions; only a strong ruler could give people direction
Locke: natural law gives people certain rights from birth, including life, liberty, and property ownership; the purpose of the government was to protect those rights; governments were based on a social contract between rulers and people
Both: natural law

Terms to Know

natural law: law that applies to everyone and can be understood by reason; social contract: an agreement between rulers and the people; separation of powers: idea that power should be divided among the branches of government

People to Meet

Thomas Hobbes: wrote about English government and society; John Locke: English thinker who wrote that government should be answerable to the people; Baron Montesquieu: French thinker who admired England's government and supported the separation of powers

Academic Vocabulary

error: something produced by mistake

Sum It Up

Government should have a separation of powers. Power should be divided among the executive, legislative, and judicial branches to keep the government from becoming too powerful and threatening people's rights.

The French Philosophes

Evaluating

Student evaluations will vary based on the philosopher they select and on their personal views. Students should show an understanding of their philosopher's ideas and should present a well-reasoned evaluation.

People to Meet

Voltaire: French philosopher and greatest Enlightenment thinker; supporter of deism; Denis Diderot: published a 28-volume encyclopedia; Mary Wollstonecraft: English writer who supported women's rights

Academic Vocabulary

topic: the subject of a discourse or of a section of a discourse; advocate: one that pleads the cause of another

Sum It Up

Voltaire opposed government supporting religion. Rousseau thought government should be based on a social contract.

Section Wrap-Up

- The Enlightenment was a period in which people came to believe that reason was a much better guide than faith or tradition.
- During the Enlightenment, political thinkers applied reason and scientific ideas to government. They spread ideas about natural law, governments based on social contract, separation of powers, freedom of speech, and the individual's right to liberty. These ideas challenged absolute monarchies.

Read to Write Challenge

Students' essays should point out that Thomas Jefferson, who wrote the Declaration of Independence, was heavily influenced by the writings of John Locke and the idea of natural rights. The writers of the Constitution were also influenced by Enlightenment ideas about government being a social contract between the people and the government.

Chapter 11, Section 3

Reading Strategy

Students should identify the Enlightenment ideas of self-government and a representative form of government as determining factors in leading the American, and later the French, people to revolt against their government.

The Age of Absolutism

Skimming

Answers will vary. Students should use headings, terms, and other clues in the text to describe the reading. Descriptions may include the idea of absolutism, enlightened despots, and specific rulers, including the Hapsburg rulers, Peter I and Catherine II, Louis XIV, and Frederick the Great.

Terms to Know

absolutism: system in which monarchs held absolute power and claimed to rule by divine right

People to Meet

Louis XIV: King of France for 72 years, known as the Sun King; Frederick II: famous Prussian ruler; Catherine II: queen of Russia who was also known as Catherine the Great

Places to Locate
Prussia: powerful German state ruled by Frederick the Great; Austria: powerful German state ruled by the Hapsburgs; St. Petersburg: Russian city founded by Peter I

Terms to Review
Sample sentence:
Joseph II freed Austria's serfs from their work for the nobles.

Sum It Up
Absolute monarchs believed they held absolute power. Enlightenment ideas said that monarchs had, by natural law, a social contract with the people. Rulers should have limited power and should answer to their people.

Revolution and Enlightenment

Monitoring Comprehension
Merchants set up colonies to make money
People wanted religious freedom
People wanted to escape economic problems in England, such as unemployment
Could own land for themselves

Terms to Know
representative government: government in which people elect representatives to make laws and conduct business; constitution: written plan of government; popular sovereignty: idea that government receives its powers from the people; estate: class; bourgeoisie: middle classes

People to Meet
George Washington: named head of the Continental Army, from Virginia; Thomas Jefferson: wrote the Declaration of Independence

Academic Vocabulary
tension: barely controlled hostility

Sum It Up
The colonists were frustrated when Britain tried to impose taxes on them. Although colonists tried to settle their differences with Great Britain, the king would not cooperate and allow them to govern themselves.

The Enlightenment's Legacy

Questioning
1. Q: What groups could not vote early in American history? A: women and African Americans
2. Q: Who was Martin Luther King, Jr.? A: an important civil rights leader in the 1950s and 1960s
3. Q: Why was the United Nations formed? A: to encourage countries to settle disagreements peacefully and to support human rights around the world

Sum It Up
King used the Enlightenment ideas of reason and human rights to argue that all people should have equal opportunities.

Section Wrap-up
- The Magna Carta, the English Bill of Rights, and Enlightenment ideas from Locke, Hobbes, Montesquieu, and others influenced Americans.
- England repeatedly taxed the colonies and did not give them representation in their government. The colonists believed that King George III had violated their rights and that they had the right to rebel.
- Enlightenment ideas were the basis for the formation of the United Nations, which works to promote human rights and peacefully resolve conflicts between nations. They also influence the development of science and technology, which constantly find new ways to increase our knowledge and improve peoples' lives.

Read to Write Challenge
Students' essays should focus on the United Nations, why it was founded, and what its primary goals are. They should also mention how the rational approach is still used in scientific research and the development of new technologies.